MUSCULAR STRENGTH
AND
ENDURANCE IN MAN

Prentice-Hall., Inc.   *Englewood Cliffs, New Jersey*

INTERNATIONAL

RESEARCH MONOGRAPH SERIES

IN PHYSICAL EDUCATION

Franklin Henry, *Editor*

Muscular Strength
and
Endurance in Man

H. HARRISON CLARKE
Research Professor
of Physical Education
University of Oregon

MUSCULAR STRENGTH
AND
ENDURANCE IN MAN
H. Harrison Clarke

Library of Congress Catalog
Card Number: 66–19896

Printed in the United States of America
C–60691

Current printing (last digit):

10 9 8 7 6 5 4 3 2 1

PRENTICE-HALL INTERNATIONAL, INC., *London*
PRENTICE-HALL OF AUSTRALIA, PTY. LTD., *Sydney*
PRENTICE-HALL OF CANADA, LTD., *Toronto*
PRENTICE-HALL OF INDIA (PRIVATE) LTD., *New Delhi*
PRENTICE-HALL OF JAPAN, INC., *Tokyo*

To My Grandchildren

Stephen Harrison Clarke
Gregory Bennet Clarke
Meredith Louise Clarke
Scott Harrison Hunsdon
Tamara Faith Hunsdon

Acknowledgments

The numerous research studies upon which this monograph on "muscular strength, and endurance in man" is based were conducted by the writer or under his direction when serving as Director of Graduate Studies and Professor of Physical Education at Springfield, Massachusetts, and as Research Professor of Physical Education at the University of Oregon, Eugene, Oregon.

The research at Springfield College was subsidized from two sources: the Office of Naval Research, United States Navy Department, 1947 to 1952; and the Climatic Research Laboratory, Quartermaster Corps, Department of the Army, 1952–1954. The ergographic research at the University of Oregon was conducted in the Physical Education Research Laboratory by students working for graduate degrees; in a number of instances, grants were made by the Office of Scientific and Scholarly Research of the Graduate School. The Medford data in Chapter 6 were from the longitudinal Medford Boys' Growth Project, subsidized from 1956 to date by the Medford Public Schools, Southern Orgeon, Athletic Institute (Chicago), Curriculum Development Fund of Oregon State Department of Education, and Office of Scientific and Scholarly Research of University of Oregon.

Sincere acknowledgments are made to the many graduate and other students who participated in the research related to this monograph. Individual recognition would be most desirable were there not so many. Consequently, only those who served as staff or graduate assistants will be named here, together with their present locations.

Springfield College: Dr. Clayton T. Shay, Springfield College; Dr. Donald K. Mathews, Ohio State University; Dr. David H. Clarke, University of Maryland; Theodore L. Bailey, Climatic Research Laboratory, Army Quartermaster Corps; Dr. L. Richard Geser, University of Utah.

University of Oregon: Dr. Kay H. Petersen, Texas Western College; Dr. David H. Clarke, University of Maryland; Morgan E. Shelley, Grosmond College, Spring Valley, Calif.; Dr. Arne L. Olson, Temple University; Dr. Norman S. Watt, University of British Columbia; Dr. Richard Munroe, University of Oregon; Jan Broekhoff, University of Oregon; Dr. Etsuo Kurimoto, Juntendo University, Tokyo, Japan.

From the Medford public schools, special mention is made of the late Dr. Leonard Mayfield, former Superintendent of Schools, Elliott Becken, Superintendent, and Lee Ragsdale, Director of Physical Education. Also, recognition is given to Dr. Theodore G. Schopf of Southern Oregon College.

H.H.C.

Contents

**MUSCULAR STRENGTH
AND
ENDURANCE IN MAN**

Chapter 1 / **Introduction**

Importance of Strength

Man's existence and effectiveness depend upon his muscles. Volitional movements of the body or any of its parts are impossible without action by skeletal muscles. Thus, obviously, one cannot stand, walk, run, jump, climb, or swim without the contraction of many muscles throughout the body. Smaller muscles perform intricate functions, including writing manuscripts, playing musical instruments, singing, using hand tools, catching and throwing balls, and the like. Muscles perform vital functions of the body. The heart is a muscle; death occurs instantly when it ceases to contract. Breathing, digestion, and elimination would be impossible without muscular contractions.

The good condition of muscles, their strength and endurance, is essential to man. Too frequently, this fact is ignored in an automated society, as only minimal muscular strength and endurance are needed functionally to perform many tasks. However, a sedentary society, in which the muscles are used only mildly, seldom vigorously, is conducive to physical degeneration. While Kraus coined the phrase earlier, Kraus and Raab (68) extensively developed the concept of "hypokinetic disease," defined as the "whole spectrum of inactivity-induced somatic and mental derangements." They developed the thesis that physical activity is a prerequisite for healthful living, that lack of it is in part responsible for disease, and that lack of exercise constitutes a cause for a deficiency state comparable to avitaminosis. In fact, a relatively new medical specialty, physical medicine and rehabilitation, makes extensive use of exercise as the therapeutic modality.

A number of researches support the contention that physical vigor is related to mental accomplishments, especially as affecting mental alertness. Thus, it may be contended that a person's general learning potential for a given level of intelligence is increased or decreased in accordance with his physical vitality. A similar relationship is evident between strength, an essential component of physical fitness, and social adjustment. From the Institute of Child Welfare, the University of California at Berkeley, Jones (66) reported that boys high in strength tend to be well adjusted socially and psychologically; boys low in strength show tendencies toward social difficulties, feelings of inferiority, and other personal maladjustments. Studies conducted at the United States Military Academy by Appleton (1) indicate that physical proficiency measures are useful predictors of nonacademic aspects of military success.

Numerous studies show that muscular strength and endurance are essential factors in athletic success. This fact is now accepted by many champion athletes in various sports who train regularly on weights to reach and maintain high levels of muscular condition.

Thus, it may be recognized that the strength and endurance of muscles is prerequisite to human effectiveness in many ways. This monograph is intended to provide some additional knowledge about muscular strength and endurance as manifested volitionally by man.

Measurement of Strength

Hunsicker and Donnelly (64) have described the various devices used to measure the strength of skeletal muscles as volitionally manifested by man. Certain types of the early instruments are in use today, especially back and leg dynamometers and various manuometers.

According to the historical account by Hunsicker and Donnelly, the first person to use an instrument known as a dynamometer was an Englishman named Graham. As adapted by Desaguliers, this device consisted of a large wooden frame supported by uprights, which also offered points of resistance; handles were attached to a crossbar which moved a steelyard; the amount of force used could be determined and regulated by hanging weights on the crossbar.

The forerunner of the spring dynamometers in use today was produced in 1807 by Regnier. This instrument was utilized to measure grip strength, pulling power of the arm muscles, and lifting power of the back muscles. Sargent initiated strength testing at Harvard University in 1880. He used an instrument similar to Regnier's dynamometer for measuring back and leg strength; for testing grip strength, a compact manuometer, small enough to fit inside a person's hand was utilized. With an adapter, this grip dynamometer was also used to test arm-pushing and arm-pulling strengths. The spring-type back and leg dynamometer was improved over the years; and, several types of grip dynamometers were devised, including the Collin eliptical spring steel instrument, the Smedley adjustable grip device, and the Narragansett manuometer.

Recent instruments proposed for strength measurement include the cable tensiometer, the Newman myometer, and various strain-gauge arrangements. These instruments will be described and discussed later in this monograph. Devices for testing muscular endurance will also be considered in subsequent chapters.

Scope of the Monograph

The purpose of this monograph is to present studies related to the muscular strength and muscular endurance of man conducted by the writer or under his direction over a period of 20 years. As will be readily seen from the references, many of these studies have been published individually in various journals over this time-span. In a number of instances, however, materials have not been published before. In a sense, then, this monograph draws these researches together as a rather extensive synthesis.

The muscular strength studies presented here are limited to those conducted by cable-tension testing methods. For this method of testing, as described in Chapter 2, the subject pulls maximally on a light cable; the tension applied is recorded on a tensiometer. Studies by the investigator utilizing other strength testing instruments such as the dynamometer and the manuometer are not included in the monograph.

The definition of muscular strength proposed is *the tension muscles can apply in a single maximum contraction*. Strength by this definition provides the basis for all strength studies reported. However, various applications of this "maximum-tension principle" have been made. Thus, in some studies, the strength a given muscle group can apply when the body is positioned in one or more specified ways is studied. In other studies, strength tests given before and after fatiguing activity indicate the amount of resultant muscular fatigue. In each instance, a strength test constitutes an essential testing element.

Muscular endurance is defined as *the ability of muscles to continue work*. Two variations of muscular endurance are recognized: *isometric*, whereby a maximum static muscular contraction is held; and *isotonic*, whereby the muscles continue to raise and lower a submaximal load. In the isometric form, the muscles maintain a fixed length; in the isotonic form, they alternately shorten and lengthen.

In this monograph, the muscular endurance studies involve the isotonic type; the studies are further confined to those utilizing the Kelso-Hellebrandt ergograph as the testing instrument. This device permits the subject to continue raising a submaximal load until volitionally unable to do so. Kymograph tracings may be obtained and a meter permits recording the cumulative distance the load is lifted in a single exercise bout.

In the conduct of these studies, only the *volitional* muscular efforts of human subjects were measured. Efforts were made to obtain "all-out" responses of the various subjects in a given testing situation. The method of motivating the subjects was consistently maintained; this method involved proper instructions before testing and verbal encouragement during testing.

Organization

This first chapter of the monograph provides an orientation to the studies to be presented; the seventh chapter assembles conclusions that may be drawn from the results of these studies. Each of the five intervening chapters deals with a specific phase of the problems under investigation.

Chapter 2 describes the origins of the cable-tension strength tests. In addition to the construction of 38 strength tests of muscle groups throughout the body, these investigations provide information related to the body positions permitting the most effective application of muscle strength. Considerable attention is given to the contractile power of muscles throughout the range of motion of the joints they activate.

Muscular endurance studies with the ergograph are described in Chapter 3. A brief account of the origins of ergography and the development of the Kelso-Hellebrandt ergographs is provided. Studies leading to the effective utilization of the Kelso-Hellebrandt ergograph in single-bout testing to volitional exhaustion are explained. These studies bring together the tensiometer and the ergograph, as it was found that the ergograph weight load for a given subject could best be determined as a proportion of the strength of the muscles to be exercised, as measured by cable-tension methods. Finally, in this chapter studies of the conditioning effects from controlled ergographic exercise are presented.

In Chapter 4, investigations of the strength decrement manifestations of muscle fatigue are presented. In these studies, again, both the tensiometer and the Kelso-Hellebrandt ergograph were utilized. Muscle fatigue was induced by prescribed ergographic exercise; the degree of muscle fatigue was evaluated as the resultant strength decrement, determined as the difference between pre- and post-exercise strength of the muscles exercised. Studies of the threshold levels of muscular fatigue and the effects of various motivational situations upon ergographic performances are included.

The Strength Decrement Index is established in Chapter 4 as a test of muscular fatigue. This index is the percentage of strength loss from fatiguing activity as obtained from strength scores before and after exercise. In Chapter 5, applications of the Strength Decrement Index are made to the fatigue of muscles involved in various physical activities. The activities studied include pack carrying on military marches, all-out swimming, and submaximal treadmill running. In a sense, then, this chapter is a continuation of the preceding one.

In Chapter 6, various muscular strength and muscular fatigue relationships are presented. In the main, only muscular strength relationships involving the cable-tension type of strength testing are included; for muscular fatigue relationships, mostly studies in strength decrement are reported. The studies include: intercorrelations of strength tests; correlations of strength tests with physical-motor measures, athletic ability, and maturity; muscular fatigue relationships; and muscular strength-endurance relationships.

Chapter *2* / Body Positions and Strength Applications

The measurement of muscular strength, that is, of the contractile power of muscles in a single maximum effort, is centuries old. In this chapter, the origins of one of the newer forms, cable-tension strength tests, are described. Then, studies of strength in which this strength-testing method was utilized are presented.

Cable-Tension Strength Tests

The construction of strength tests utilizing the tensiometer was originated during World War II in the Army Air Force convalescent hospital physical reconditioning service, in order to test the strength of individual muscle groups involved in orthopedic disabilities. At that time, a review of orthopedic strength tests indicated limited availability of objective techniques. Daniels, Williams, and Worthingham (43) reviewed extensively and analyzed critically "manual" strength tests proposed between 1912 and 1946. Nearly all of these tests were dependent upon the judgment of the examiner as he estimated the ability of the muscle to overcome gravity and outside force. In 1915, Lovett and Martin (70) proposed spring-balance tests for measuring the strength of 22 muscle groups. Elbel (49) utilized a Chatillon spring scale for this same purpose.

By use of the tensiometer, Clarke and Peterson (19) attempted to improve the objectivity and validity of orthopedic strength tests. Initially, such tests were empirically derived for 28 muscle groups.

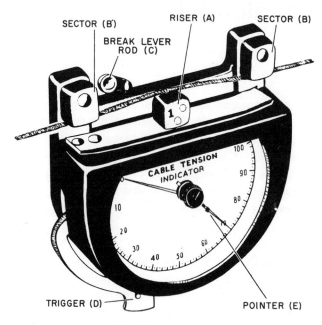

Fig. 2.1 Tensiometer

Testing Equipment

TENSIOMETER. The cable tensiometer (Fig. 2.1) is a small compact unit (4″ × 4″ × 1¼″) originally designed to test the tension of aircraft control cables.* Cable tension is determined by measuring the force applied to a riser and causing an offset in a cable stretched taut between two sectors. The tension is then converted into pounds on a calibration chart supplied with the instrument.

* Manufactured by Pacific Scientific Company, Bell Gardens, California.

The manufacturer adapted the tensiometer for strength testing in the following ways: (a) special calibration for an "up-pull" on the cable, rather than for placement on a taut cable, (b) addition of a maximum pointer to facilitate reading the subject's score, and (c) deletion of the brake lever rod, as this is needed only to fix the original pointer after applying the instrument to a taut cable.

OTHER EQUIPMENT. Besides a tensiometer, the following items of equipment are needed for cable-tension strength testing: a specially designed testing table, various pulling assemblies, a goniometer, and special items for testing finger movements and supination and pronation of the forearm. The most up-to-date descriptions of these items with instructions for their construction are provided by Clarke and Clarke (28).

Strength Tests

After the wartime convalescent hospital applications, extensive research was conducted in the development of cable-tension strength tests. Thirty-eight tests were eventually proposed to measure the strength of muscle groups activating the following joints of the body: finger, thumb, wrist, forearm, elbow, shoulder, neck, trunk, hip, knee, and ankle (16, 19, 27). The current techniques for these tests are described and illustrated in H. Harrison Clarke and David H. Clarke, *Developmental and Adapted Physical Education* (Englewood Cliffs, N.J.: Prentice-Hall, Inc., 1963), pp. 73–96.

Research in the construction of these tests included the following: determination of the body position which permits the greatest application of strength for each joint movement, selection of the joint angle which resulted in the strongest movement, and the study of such factors as the location of the pulling strap on the body part serving as fulcrum, and the effect of gravity on test scores. Consultation on the kinesiological determination of potentially desirable positions for each test was had with physiatrists* at the Mayo Clinic, Rochester, Minnesota; suggested changes in positions were

---

* Acknowledgment is made to Drs. Earl C. Elkins, Khalil G. Wakim, and Gordon M. Martin.

then tested for validity under laboratory conditions. For the most part, the objectivity coefficients (test-retest correlations by different testers with the same subjects) for the various tests were above .90.

Initially, under medical supervision, trials of the proposed cable-tension strength tests were made on orthopedic patients in AAF convalescent hospitals. Subsequently the tests were evaluated for application to patients at the U.S. Naval Hospital, Chelsea, Massachusetts. The results of the strength test trials upon patients were considered satisfactory by medical specialists; in general, these results coincided well with medical opinion of patient status.

While the cable-tension tests were originally intended for the measurement of the strength of muscles involved in orthopedic disabilities, other uses for them have subsequently been found. As will be seen in this monograph, their utilization for research into the volitional muscular strength of humans is important. They continue to maintain their usefulness in evaluating the results of therapeutic exercise.

Comparison of Testing Instruments

Instruments

While the tensiometer was adapted by the writer for conducting research into volitional muscular strength manifestations, this instrument was compared with the Wakim-Porter strain gauge, a spring scale, and the Newman myometer for effectiveness in recording strength (15). These other instruments are described below.

WAKIM-PORTER STRAIN GAUGE (89). Strain-gauge devices are based on the fact that a wire changes its electrical resistance when stretched. Such devices have been proposed by a number of investigators.

Ralston and associates (79) devised such an instrument in 1947 to study the strength of isolated muscles of upper-arm amputees with cineplastic tunnels. A year later, Carlson and Martin (7) developed an apparatus for eliciting a stretch reflex and recording electrically the isometric responses of the muscles by means of strain gauges. Tuttle and associates (87, 88) utilized load cells, based on strain gauges, for the dynamometric measurement of the maximum strength and isometric endurance of grip, back, and leg muscles. Beasley (4) developed an electromyodynagraph utilizing strain gauges in load cells, with which he was able to study the isometric responses of 40 muscular actions. The Anthropology Section of the Aero-Medical Laboratory of Wright-Patterson Air Force Base designed a "Kinematic Muscle Study Machine" employing strain gauges, which tests forces in three directions at once (63).

The Wakim-Porter strain gauge, which was used in this investigation, utilizes four strain-gauge elements; two are attached to the inside and two to the outside of an aluminum alloy ring (4 cm. in diameter, 2 cm. in width, and 2.6 mm. in thickness). The ring is covered with a protective layer of friction tape; sturdy attachments are made to the ring for its incorporation into the strength test pulling assembly. The strain-gauge elements are connected by four separate wires to complete a circuit containing a galvanometer, a battery, and a 20-watt bulb. In strength testing, the aluminum ring is distorted from the tension applied to it; this distortion stretches the strain gauges, causing deflections within the galvanometer. Two "slivers" of light are produced by light from the 20-watt bulb reflecting on the galvanometer. In this study, these slivers of light were reflected on a frosted plastic scale, marked off in millimeters: one sliver remained fixed at the zero point; the other deflected along the scale with the amount of resistance applied to the ring. (In the original Wakim-Porter arrangement, instead of on a plastic scale, performance was recorded on photostat paper. Exposure was made by the slivers of light reflecting through a slit in a box containing a slowly revolving roll of photostat paper.)

In studies completed by Wakim and associates (89), their strain-gauge arrangement had higher readings than the tensiometer in 183 of 200 strength tests of the elbow flexor muscles; the average difference was 4.1 pounds.

SPRING SCALE. An ordinary spring scale with a capacity of 100 pounds was used in this study. A ring was located at each end of the scale to permit incorporation into the pulling assembly. A maximum pointer was added which slid freely with the pointer on the scale when testing and remained stationary at the farthest point reached in a pull.

NEWMAN MYOMETER. The Newman myometer (76) consists of a cylindrical housing 2 inches in diameter and 3¼ inches long, which encloses the complete mechanism. Extending from one end is a shaft with a pressure-transmitting button. Enclosed at the other end and visible through a transparent plastic cover is a dial gauge. A built-in hydraulic pressure converter transmits the linear force exerted on the button to the pressure gauge. Each myometer set consists of two instruments with capacities of 15 and 60 pounds. In testing, the tester pushes the transmitting button against the body part serving as a lever for the muscles being tested; the score is recorded at the point where the subject "breaks," that is, gives way to the pressure being applied.

Procedures

An especially designed device for calibrating the testing instruments was obtained from the manufacturer of the tensiometer. This calibrator is equipped with a standard spring dynamometer of proven accuracy. With the exception of the myometer, the testing instruments were given a common calibration with this device.

Six strength tests were utilized in this study; these tests were selected so as to include both weak and strong muscular movements. The weak movements were finger flexion, wrist dorsal flexion, shoulder outward rotation, and neck extension; the strong movements were knee extension and ankle plantar flexion. Inasmuch as certain of the testing instruments had capacity limitations (100 pounds for the spring scale and 60 pounds for the myometer*), these devices could only be used for the weak movements. The spring scale was utilized

---

* Actually, the myometer utilized in this study was limited to 48 pounds.

for neck extension and wrist dorsal flexion strength tests only; and the myometer, for finger flexion and wrist dorsal flexion strength tests only.

The subjects were 64 nondisabled Springfield College men.

Results

In the conduct of this study, three procedures were followed as described below.

OBJECTIVITY COEFFICIENTS. Objectivity coefficients, in the form of coefficients of correlation between repeated tests by different testers, were obtained for the different instruments on the various tests. The tensiometer proved to be the most consistent of the four devices; the objectivity coefficients for the six strength tests varied between .90 and .96.

In general, the objectivity coefficients for the strain gauge were satisfactory. However, three of the coefficients were below .90; these were .87 for neck extension, .85 for wrist dorsal flexion, and .81 for knee extension strength tests. The strain gauge was much more sensitive to slight changes in tension than were the other instruments, even to the point of being affected by changes in room temperature. Thus, this instrument needed calibration before each testing session.

The objectivity coefficients for the two strength tests in which the spring scale was utilized were comparable to those obtained for the tensiometer (.91 and .97). The coefficients for the myometer were .82 for finger flexion and .79 for wrist dorsal flexion strengths.

MEAN-STRENGTH RECORDS. The mean differences in strength recorded by the four instruments for the various tests were determined and tested for significance by application of the *t* ratio. A *t* ratio of 2.00 is necessary for significance at the .05 level. In each instance, the mean for the tensiometer was taken as the basis of reference for the others. These results are presented in Table 2.1.

The tensiometer and strain gauge were used for all six strength

Table 2.1

COMPARISON OF MEAN POUNDS OF STRENGTH RECORDED BY
FOUR STRENGTH TESTING INSTRUMENTS

Strength Test	Tensiom- eter	Strain Gauge	Spring Scale	Newman Myometer	Mean Diff.	t Ratio
Weak Movements						
Finger flexion	36.23	43.71			— 7.48	— 3.40
	36.23			18.98	17.25	16.52
Wrist dorsal	44.50	44.54			— 0.04	— 0.03
flexion	44.50			40.16	4.34	3.90
Shoulder outward	47.98	48.35			— 0.37	— 0.22
rotation	47.98		42.66		5.32	6.24
Neck extension	54.82	59.14			— 4.32	— 2.52
	54.82		50.42		4.40	5.37
Strong Movements						
Knee extension	237.30	224.50			12.80	4.60
Ankle plantar						
flexion	224.00	216.20			7.80	3.08

tests; further, the two instruments were coupled in the testing, so that both recorded from the same pull. For the strong movements, the tensiometer was definitely superior to the strain gauge in the amount of strength recorded. The *t* ratios for the differences between means were 4.60 for knee extension strength and 3.08 for ankle plantar flexion strength; these differences exceeded the .01 level of significance.

For the weaker movements, the superiority of either the tensiometer or the strain gauge was not decisive. The strain gauge produced significantly higher means for two strength tests, finger flexion and neck extension. For the other two weak movements, however, significant mean differences were not obtained. Subsequently, an attempt was made to account for the inconsistencies in results obtained with these two instruments. Distortion of the aluminum ring resulting from pulling on it disappeared slowly, a condition which was especially pronounced when testing strong movements. Any strength test given while the ring still had some distortion, therefore, would result in higher test scores.

Compared with the spring scale in two movements, the tensiometer had significantly higher strength test means. The *t* ratios for the differences between means were 6.24 for shoulder outward rotation strength and 5.37 for neck extension strength. The differences in results obtained by these two instruments are attributed to the pronounced movement of the spring-scale testing unit when tension is applied. This movement permits the subject's joint to move beyond the degree specified for each test. Also, such movement allows a change in the 90-degree angle of pull required for all tests. With the tensiometer, these angles are reasonably well stabilized.

For both finger-flexion and wrist-dorsal-flexion strength tests, the tensiometer recorded significantly higher means than did the myometer. Considerable difficulty was encountered in obtaining a consistent application of the myometer.

INTERINSTRUMENT CORRELATIONS. The correlations between the scores obtained with the tensiometer and the strain gauge were low for the four weak strength tests, ranging from .14 to .43. The results with the strong movements were high, with coefficients of .89 for knee-extension strength and .91 for ankle-plantar-flexion strength. The low interinstrument correlations for the weak movements could well be due, in part at least, to the ring-distortion situation described above.

Correlations between the tensiometer and the spring scale were .80 for neck extension strength and .58 for shoulder outward rotation strength. Correlations between the tensiometer and the myometer were .14 and .36 for finger-flexion and wrist-dorsal-flexion strength tests respectively.

Conclusions

Evaluations of the four strength testing instruments resulting from this study follow.

TENSIOMETER. As reflected by objectivity coefficients, the tensiometer has the greatest precision for all strength tests. It is the most stable and generally useful of the instruments; and it is free of faults found in the other devices.

WAKIM-PORTER STRAIN GAUGE. The strain gauge correlates well with the tensiometer in strength testing of the stronger muscle groups; however, the mean scores obtained for these tests were significantly lower. This instrument is most sensitive to slight tensions, including changes in room temperature. Distortion of the aluminum ring used with the strain gauges results from strength testing; further, the ring returns slowly to its original shape, especially after strong strength efforts have been made.

SPRING SCALE. The spring scale used in this study was limited to 100 pounds; scales with greater capacity could be utilized but would probably be increasingly awkward and insensitive to weak strength efforts. The objectivity coefficients are satisfactory. A serious fault of this instrument is the amount of movement of the testing unit when tension is applied; this allows specified joint angles and the angle of pull to change for the various strength tests. Thus, lower scores result, differing proportionately from subject to subject depending upon their strength.

NEWMAN MYOMETER. The use of the myometer is based upon resistance to pressure rather than application of tension by pulling, as for the other instruments. By construction, its capacity is 60 pounds. Objectivity coefficients are fairly high when testers are well trained. Mean scores with this instrument are significantly lower than for the tensiometer.

Body Position and Strength Application

In the construction of the cable-tension strength tests, the body positions for the best application of strength were critically reviewed for the various joint movements. Kinesiological analyses of these positions were made by the physiatrists at the Mayo Clinic mentioned above (30). Suggested changes in the tests were then validated, as described in this section. This study of muscle action has basic interest to physical educators, physical therapists, kinesiologists, orthopedic physicians, and doctors of physical medicine and rehabilitation (physiatrists).

In presenting the results of this investigation of body position for the strongest application of muscular strength, illustrations will be used to clarify the various positions studied. Final test positions depicted will not always conform to the test descriptions in one respect, the joint angle specified. Such joint angles were later changed as a result of the joint-angle study described in the next section of this chapter. In obtaining certain of the test scores given below, a "gravity factor" has been added or subtracted. This factor is the weight of a body part which is either lifted or "weighed in" when making the movement. The weight of the body part was determined at the test position by weighing it with the tensiometer.

Shoulder Flexion

POSITIONS. *Position A* (Fig. 2.2): Subject in supine position, hips and knees flexed, with feet resting on table, free arm on chest; arm being tested flexed at shoulder joint to 135 degrees, elbow in thrust position. *Position B:* Subject in same position as A, except humerus rotated inward by turning forearm across chest, hand held low to opposite shoulder. The purpose of this change was to eliminate the effect of the biceps muscle in the shoulder flexion movement.

RESULTS. The mean strength obtained for Position A was 77.13 pounds; for Position B, 73.50 pounds. The difference between the means of 3.63 pounds was not significant, since the t ratio was 1.13. Thus, the effect of the biceps muscle in this movement was not established.

Shoulder Adduction

POSITIONS. *Position A:* Subject in supine position, hips and knees flexed, with feet resting on table, free arm on chest; arm being tested adducted at shoulder joint to 160 degrees, forearm in

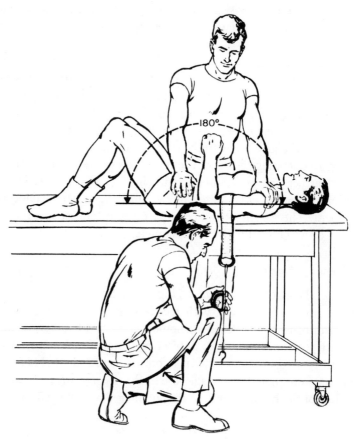

Fig. 2.2   Shoulder flexion

thrust position. *Position B* (Fig. 2.3): Subject in same position as A, except humerus rotated inward by turning forearm across chest, hand held low toward opposite shoulder. The purpose of this change was to eliminate the effect of the biceps muscle in the shoulder adduction movement.

RESULTS. The mean strength obtained for Position A was 63.00 pounds; for Position B, 52.25 pounds. The difference between the

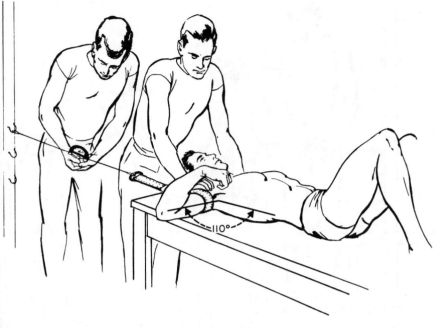

Fig. 2.3 **Shoulder adduction**

means was 10.75 pounds, a decrease of 17 per cent; the *t* ratio was 3.90. This reduction in strength was attributed to the elimination of the biceps muscle from the movement.

Trunk Flexion

POSITIONS. *Position A* (Fig. 2.4A): Subject in sitting position on chair, trunk and thighs forming right angle, arms folded on chest, hips and knees braced. *Position B* (Fig. 2.4B): Subject in supine position, hip and knee joints straight. In this body position, the trunk flexor muscles are on greater stretch.

RESULTS. The mean strength obtained for Position A was 126.68 pounds; for Position B, 226.21 pounds (gravity factor added). The

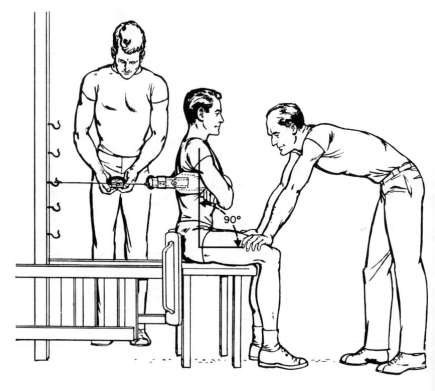

Fig. 2.4A   Trunk flexion

difference between the means was 99.53 pounds, an increase of 78 per cent; the *t* ratio was 18.47. Thus, the greater stretch of the trunk flexor muscles resulted in improved ability to apply tension.

Trunk Extension

Positions A and B for the trunk extension strength test were similar to the corresponding positions for the trunk flexion test, except the body is reversed for a trunk extension movement. The mean strength obtained for Position A was 234.66 pounds; for Position B, 271.20 pounds (gravity factor added). The difference between

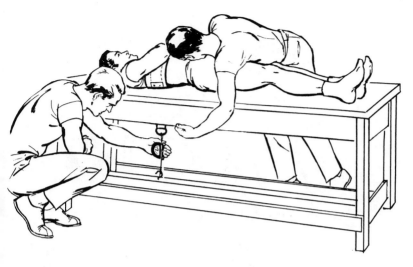

Fig. 2.4B   Trunk flexion

the means was 36.54 pounds, an increase of 16 per cent; the *t* ratio was 4.48. Thus, the trunk extensor muscles were able to apply increased tension when on greater stretch.

Trunk Lateral Flexion

POSITIONS. *Position A* (Fig. 2.5A): Subject in prone position, legs together and extended, arms at side. *Position B* (Fig. 2.5B): Subject in side-lying position, legs together and extended, under arm placed through slit in table, upper arm at side. The purpose of this change was to improve the mechanical advantage of the test.

RESULTS. The mean strength obtained for Position A was 159.19 pounds; for Position B, 220.08 pounds (gravity factor added). The difference between the means was 60.89 pounds, an increase of 38 per cent; the *t* ratio was 21.67. Thus, the mechanical advantage of the trunk lateral flexor muscles to apply tension was improved.

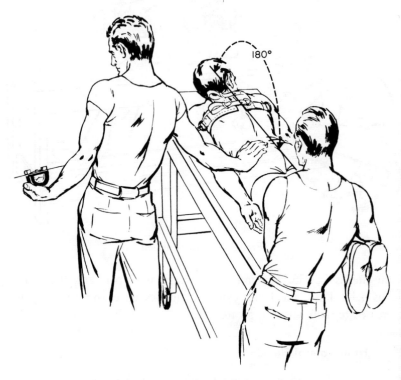

Fig. 2.5A Trunk lateral flexion

Hip Flexion

POSITIONS. *Position* A (Fig. 2.6A): Subject in supine position, leg not tested extended and resting on table, arms folded on chest; thigh being tested flexed at hip joint to 120 degrees, knee flexed with angle not specified. *Position B* (Fig. 2.6B): Subject sitting at end of table, arms extended and placed to rear with hands grasping sides of table, legs hanging free; thigh on side being tested flexed at hip joint to 90 degrees, knee joint in 90 degrees flexion. This change was made to improve the mechanical advantage of the position and

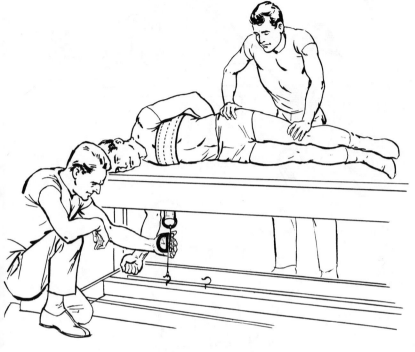

Fig. 2.5B Trunk lateral flexion

to permit greater functioning of the iliopsoas muscle in the hip flexion movement.

RESULTS. The mean strength obtained for Position A was 64.81 pounds; for Position B, 115.00 pounds. The difference between the means was 50.19 pounds, an increase of 77 per cent; the *t* ratio was 15.78. Thus, the increased power of the new position was demonstrated. It is probable that the iliopsoas muscle applies its greatest rotary force when tension is being exerted at a right angle to the longitudinal axis of the femur.

THIRD POSITION. With different subjects, Position B was compared with a third position for the hip flexion strength test. *Posi-*

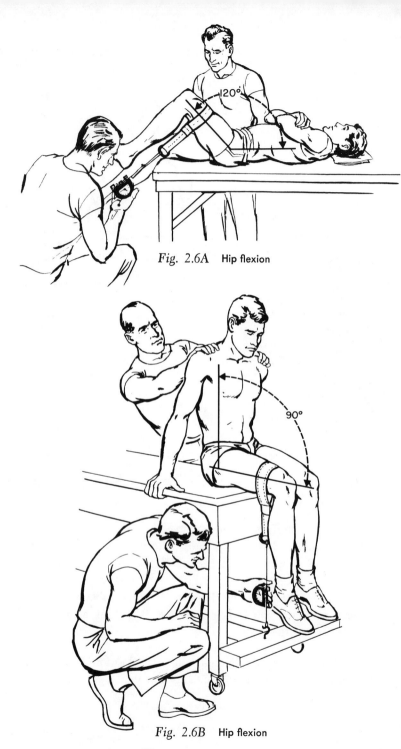

Fig. 2.6A   Hip flexion

Fig. 2.6B   Hip flexion

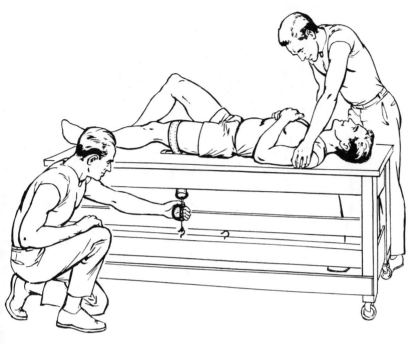

Fig. 2.6C   **Hip flexion**

tion C (Fig. 2.6C): Subject in supine position; arms folded on chest, hip and knee of free leg flexed, with foot resting on table; hip and knee of leg being tested fully extended. In this position, the hip flexor muscles were on greater stretch.

RESULTS. The mean strength obtained for Position B was 108.88 pounds; for Position C, 207.19 pounds. The difference between the means was 98.31 pounds, an increase of 90 per cent; the *t* ratio was 19.70. Thus, the effect of increased stretch of the hip flexor muscles in their application of tension was demonstrated.

Hip Extension

POSITIONS. *Position* A (Fig. 2.7A): Subject in sitting position at end of table, legs hanging free, arms folded on chest; thigh

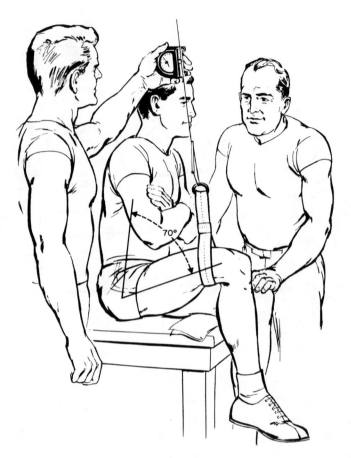

Fig. 2.7A   Hip extension

being tested flexed at hip joint to 70 degrees, knee joint flexed with angle not specified. *Position B* (Fig. 2.7B): Subject in supine position, arms folded on chest, free leg flexed at knee and hip joints, with foot resting on table; thigh being tested flexed at hip joint to 90 degrees, knee joint flexed with angle unspecified. This change was made to improve the mechanical advantage of the position.

RESULTS. The mean strength obtained for Position A was 73.25 pounds; for Position B, 130.75 pounds. The difference between the

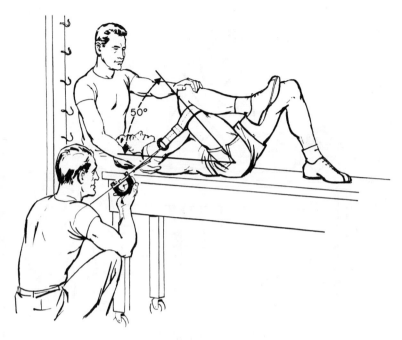

Fig. 2.7B   Hip extension

means was 57.50 pounds, an increase of 78 per cent; the *t* ratio was 8.46. Thus, the improved mechanical position for this test was reflected in improved strength application.

Subsequently, in further examination of the hip extension strength test, the hamstring muscles were thought to function if the leg was allowed to straighten at the knee joint. To check on the effect of this factor, Position B was administered to the subjects with the knee angle uncontrolled and with the leg held close to the thigh. The strength applied in the uncontrolled movement was 11.16 pounds greater than the knee-controlled movement, which was just significant at the .05 level.

THIRD POSITION. With different subjects, Position B was compared with a third position for the hip extension strength test. *Position C* (Fig. 2.7C): Subject in prone position with arms along side.

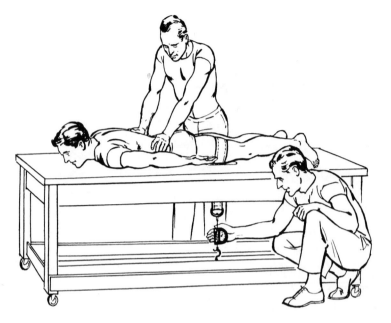

Fig. 2.7C   **Hip extension**

In Position B, the quadriceps muscles are in a shortened position and the hamstrings offer a countertension; in Position C, these situations are largely avoided.

RESULTS. The mean strength obtained for Position B was 174.90 pounds (gravity factor subtracted); for Position C, 224.17 pounds (gravity factor added). The difference between the means was 49.27 pounds, an increase of 28 per cent; the *t* ratio was 7.66. Thus, the improved functioning of the hip extensor muscles was aided by this change of position.

Hip Adduction

POSITIONS. *Position* A (Fig. 2.8A) : Subject in supine position, legs hanging free over end of table, arms folded on chest; thigh being tested adducted at hip joint to 160 degrees. *Position* B (Fig.

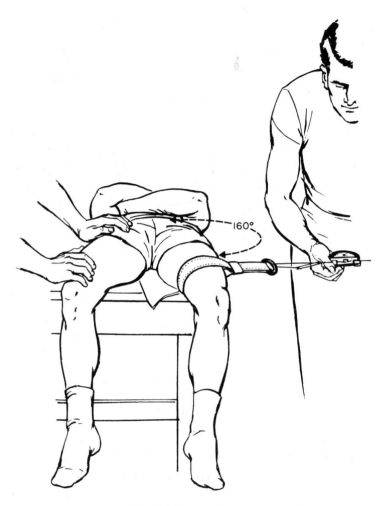

Fig. 2.8A **Hip adduction**

2.8B): Subject in same position as A, except entire body resting on table. This change in body position was tried in order to avoid an awkward position which was thought to interfere with good performance.

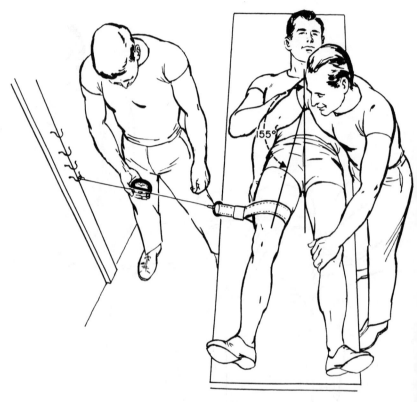

Fig. 2.8B **Hip adduction**

RESULTS. The mean strength obtained for Position A was 58.81 pounds; for Position B, 69.88 pounds. The difference between the means was 11.07 pounds, an increase of 22 per cent; the *t* ratio was 4.16. Thus, hip adductor muscles were able to perform better at the changed position.

THIRD POSITION. With different subjects, Position B was compared with a third position for the hip adduction strength test. *Position C* (Fig. 2.8C): Subject in side lying position. In this position the hip adductor muscles are on greater stretch.

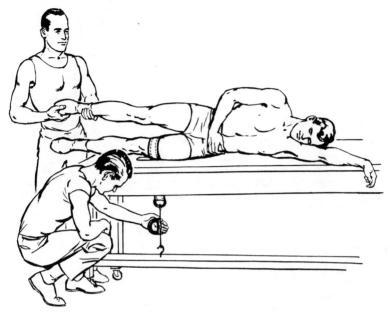

Fig. 2.8C **Hip adduction**

RESULTS. The mean strength obtained for Position B was 111.60 pounds; for Position C, 166.38 pounds (gravity factor added). The difference between the means was 54.78 pounds, an increase of 49 per cent; the *t* ratio was 16.70. Thus, the greater stretch of the hip adductor muscles improved the strength they could apply.

Hip Abduction

The various positions for the hip abduction strength test were similar to those of the hip adduction test. The results for the three positions studied were also comparable.

Knee Flexion

POSITIONS. *Position* A: Subject in prone position, legs extended beyond end of table with knee resting at edge of table; arms folded above head; leg being tested flexed at knee joint to 135 degrees,

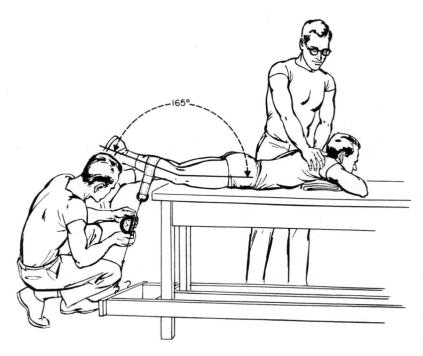

Fig. 2.9   **Knee flexion**

hips blocked by tester to prevent raising. *Position B* (Fig. 2.9):
Subject in same position as A, except block to prevent hip raising was
eliminated. It was believed that even though the hips rise during this
test, the knee flexion strength score is not affected.

RESULTS. The mean strength obtained for Position A was 95.90
pounds; for Position B, 98.88 pounds. The difference between the
means was 2.98 pounds, which was not significant since the *t* ratio
was .75. Thus, a natural raising of the hips did not affect the application of strength by the knee flexor muscles.

Knee Extension

POSITIONS. *Position A:* Subject in sitting position at end
of table, free leg hanging free, arms folded on chest; leg being tested

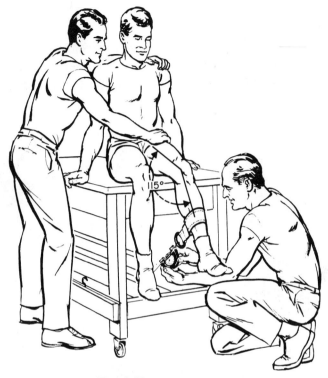

Fig. 2.10   Knee extension

flexed at knee joint to 135 degrees. *Position B* (Fig. 2.10): Subject in same position as A, except leaning backward grasping sides of table, elbows locked. With the hip at 90 degrees in Position A, the quadriceps muscles are shortened and the hamstring muscles offer counter-tension; in Position B, the quadriceps are more nearly at their full length and the tension of the hamstrings is not so great.

RESULTS. The mean strength obtained for Position A was 112.94 pounds; for Position B, 147.94 pounds. The difference between the means was 35.00 pounds, an increase of 31 per cent; the *t* ratio was 4.86. Thus, the greater stretch of the quadriceps muscles improved their ability to apply tension.

Ankle Dorsi Flexion

POSITIONS. *Position* A (Fig. 2.11A): Subject in prone position, free leg extended at knee joint to 180 degrees, arms resting on table at side of head; leg being tested flexed at knee joint to 90

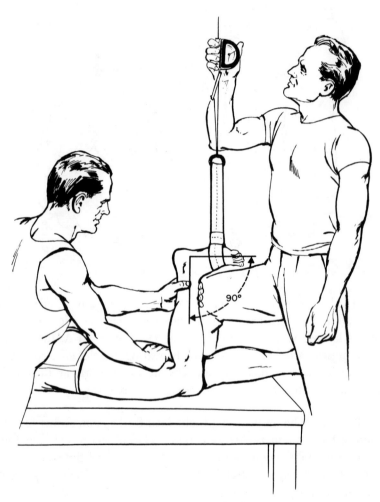

Fig. 2.11A   Ankle dorsi flexion

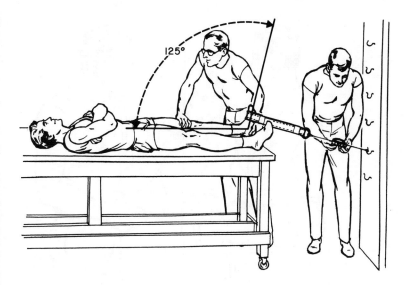

Fig. 2.11B

degrees, ankle joint in 90 degrees dorsi flexion. *Position B* (Fig. 2.11B): Subject in supine position, legs extended at hip and knee joints to 180 degrees, arms folded on chest; foot being tested dorsi flexed at ankle joint to 90 degrees. This change in body position was tried in order to avoid an awkward position which was thought to interfere with good performance.

RESULTS. The mean strength obtained for Position A was 53.72 pounds; for Position B, 71.79 pounds. The difference between the means was 17.97 pounds, an increase of 33 per cent; the t ratio was 6.44. Thus, the ankle dorsi flexor muscles were able to perform better in the changed position.

Ankle Plantar Flexion

POSITIONS. *Position A* (Fig. 2.12A): Subject in sitting position at end of table, legs hanging free, arms folded on chest; knee joint of foot being tested in 90 degrees flexion, ankle joint in 90 degrees flexion. *Position B* (Fig. 2.12B): Subject in supine position,

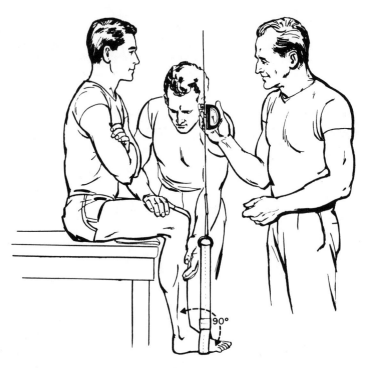

Fig. 2.12A   Plantar flexion at ankle joint

legs extended at hip and knee joints to 180 degrees, arms folded on chest; foot being tested dorsi flexed at ankle joint to 90 degrees. With the knee at 90 degrees flexion in Position A, there is considerable loss of tension in the gastrocnemius muscle; in Position B, this muscle is on greater stretch.

RESULTS. The mean strength obtained for Position A was 61.84 pounds; the mean for Position B was 129.50 pounds. The difference between the means was 67.66 pounds, an increase of 109 per cent. Thus, the position permitting greater stretch of the gastrocnemius muscle resulted in much greater application of tension in the ankle plantar flexion movement.

Subsequently, the ankle plantar flexion strength test was further improved by utilizing sturdy blocks to stabilize the shoulders, rather

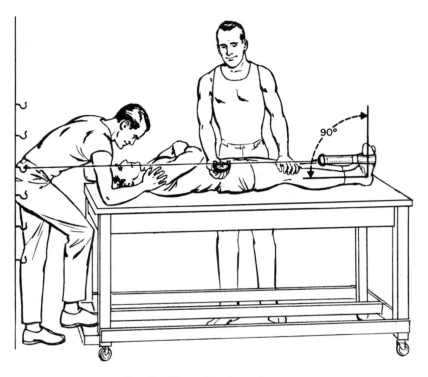

Fig. 2.12B **Ankle plantar flexion**

than their being braced by a tester, and by providing a stirrup in the pulling strap to prevent pinching the foot. In a pack-carrying study with college men as subjects, most of whom were majoring in physical education, the median strength score for this form of the test was 390 pounds; the highest strength score reported was 550 pounds. (While taking the ankle plantar flexion test, however, these subjects wore rugged military combat boots.)

Joint Angles

In the initial work on the cable-tension strength tests, joint angles were empirically selected after a brief trial of two or more positions. In order to determine these locations precisely, the muscle strength exerted throughout the full range of joint motion for fourteen of the tests was determined. Where movement through 180 degrees was possible in a joint, and permitted in the test position, nine angles 20 to 25 degrees apart were employed. Near the angle for the original test position, angles 10 degrees apart were usually used. Means were computed for each of these positions. The angle of pull was always at right angles to the body part serving as fulcrum.

In the strength tests for the joint angle study, the gravity factor was not controlled, although its effect on the knee flexion and extension strength curves is illustrated. Thus, in some tests, the weight of the limb is lifted in the movement; in others, the weight is included in the test score; and in still others, the amount of weight involved in the movement is slight or nonexistent. As a consequence, the absolute strength of the muscles is not recorded in this research, although it may be considered that the functional application of strength is demonstrated.

Fatigue from repeated maximal exertions of the same muscles was reduced by spaced testing and was equalized by systematically changing the sequence of tests for the various subjects (Latin square). The subjects were 64 nondisabled college men.

Graphs (26) were prepared showing the mean muscle strength exerted throughout the range of motion of the joints tested. In general, three types of strength curves were found, as follows: (a) ascending curves; that is, increase in strength on motion of the joint from angles of 0 to 180 degrees; (b) descending curves; and (c) ascending-descending curves, with greatest strength exhibited in the center of the range of motion.* There were individual variations of pitch and plateau within these classifications.

Ascending Curves

Strength tests for six joint movements revealed ascending curves. Four of these, hip flexion, hip abduction, knee flexion, and

---

* Zero degrees is a position away from the median line of the body; 180 degrees parallels the median line. Thus, for example, at 0 degrees in shoulder movements, the arm is over the head; and at 180 degrees it is alongside the body.

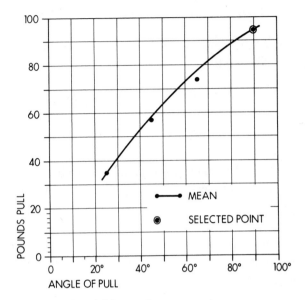

Fig. 2.13   Hip flexion strength curve

ankle dorsi flexion, had steep pitches. For the other two ascending curves, shoulder flexion and shoulder abduction, the strength was lowest at 0 degrees, rose for a distance to a plateau in the center, and finally rose again to 180 degrees.

HIP FLEXION (Fig. 2.13). The position for the hip flexion strength test was: Subject sitting at end of table, arms extended to rear with hands grasping sides of table, elbows locked (Fig. 2.6B).

This test was restricted to measuring the strength exerted from 25 degrees, thigh close to the body, to 90 degrees at a right-angle sitting position. The pitch of the curve was sharp, being a straight-line rise. Consistently greater strength was applied as the hip flexor muscles increased their stretch. The strength means of the subjects ranged from 33 pounds at 25 degrees to 95 pounds at 90 degrees; the increase was 62 pounds, or 190 per cent.

HIP ABDUCTION. The position for the hip abduction strength test was: Subject supine, free leg flexed to permit passage of cable assembly, arms folded on chest (similar to Fig. 2.8B, but for abduction).

With only three angle positions for this movement, a graph was not prepared. The results of the testing were as follows:

Angles	Means (lbs.)
135°	67
160°	77
180°	85

A fairly steep rise was found throughout this relatively short movement. The mean increase from 135 to 180 degrees was 18 pounds, or 28 per cent.

KNEE FLEXION (Fig. 2.14). The position for the knee flexion strength test was: Subject prone, lower legs extended beyond end of table, arms folded above head (Fig. 2.9).

The steep straight-line rise for the knee flexion movement levelled off between 145 and 180 degrees. As for the hip flexion test, increased strength was exerted when the muscles were on greater stretch. The strength means of the subjects ranged from 25 pounds at 50 degrees to 106 pounds at 165 degrees; the mean increase was 85 pounds, or 324 per cent.

For knee flexion, as seen in the graph, the gravity factor was added for those angles from near 90 to 170 degrees, when lifting the weight of the leg was necessary in performing the test. The slope of the curve rose more sharply than before, and the hook at the end of the curve did not appear. Thus, in the curve without gravity, the hook is attributed to the greater effort necessary in lifting the nearly straightened leg, probably at an increasing mechanical disadvantage.

ANKLE DORSI FLEXION. The position for the ankle dorsi flexion strength test was: Subject supine, legs extended at hip and knee joints to 180 degrees, arms folded on chest (Fig. 2.11B).

With only three angle positions for this movement, a graph was not prepared. The results of the testing were as follows:

Angles	Means (lbs.)
90°	56
105°	81
125°	86

Again, as the stretch of the muscles increased, the amount of strength applied became greater, although the test scores levelled off at the greatest angle of 125 degrees. The plateau is probably due to poorer leverage encountered in this position. The mean increase from 90 to 125 degrees was 30 pounds, or 54 per cent.

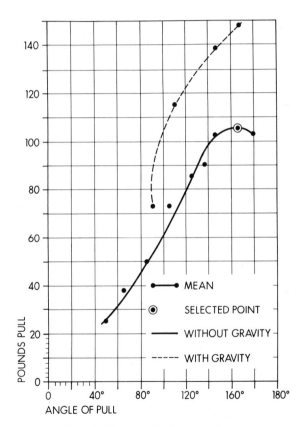

Fig. 2.14 Knee flexion strength curve

SHOULDER FLEXION (Fig. 2.15). The position for the shoulder flexion strength test was: Subject supine, hips and knees flexed, with feet resting on table, free arm on chest; elbow of arm being tested in thrust position; arm being tested adducted at shoulder joint to 180 degrees (Fig. 2.2).

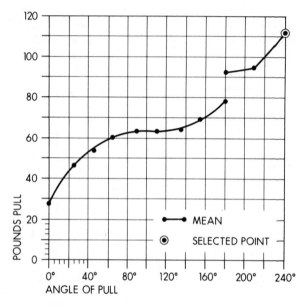

Fig. 2.15   Shoulder flexion strength curve

Initially the subjects were tested from 0 to 180 degrees. The greatest strength for this movement was applied when the arm was close to the body (180 degrees). A plateau extended from approximately 90 to 125 degrees, the effectiveness of the muscles being about the same through this range. The reduced power of the muscles of the shoulder girdle may be seen as the arm extended forward overhead. The strength means of the subjects ranged from 28 pounds at 0 degrees to 78 pounds at 180 degrees; the mean increase was 50 pounds, or 180 per cent.

Subsequently, with a different group of subjects, the strength curve was continued to 240 degrees, the arm extended backward from the median line of the body. These results are also shown in Fig. 2.15. Although a plateau occurred from 180 to 210 degrees, the strongest position for the shoulder flexion movement was with the arm extended well to the rear of the body.

SHOULDER ABDUCTION (Fig. 2.16). The position for the abduction strength test was: Subject in supine position, hips and knees flexed, with feet resting on table, free arm on chest; arm being

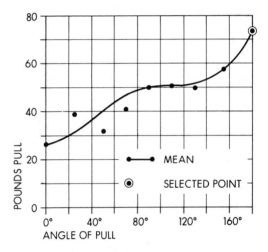

Fig. 2.16   Shoulder abduction strength curve

tested flexed at shoulder joint to 180 degrees, elbow flexed. The tester prevented elevation of shoulder by bracing with hands.

The resultant curve of strength for this movement was similar to the curve for the shoulder flexion movement: the height was at 180 degrees; a plateau occurred between 90 and 135 degrees; and the low point was at 0 degrees. Thus, as the arm extended sideward overhead, the weaker scapular rotators became less and less effective; as seen in the graph, however, all strength means did not fall on the graph line, as the arm abducted overhead. The strength means of the subjects ranged from 27 pounds at 0 degrees to 74 pounds at 180 degrees (comparable to the shoulder flexion movement); the mean increase was 47 pounds, or 170 per cent.

Descending Curves

Four of the joint movements—elbow extension, hip extension, hip adduction, and ankle plantar flexion—exhibited descending strength curves. In these curves, the greatest strength was applied when the fulcrum was away from the body; and the least, as it approached the median line. All of these showed plateaus or near plateaus.

ELBOW EXTENSION (Fig. 2.17). The position for the elbow extension strength test was: Subject supine, hips and knees flexed, with feet resting on table, free arm on chest; arm being tested flexed and adducted at shoulder joint to 180 degrees. By appropriate bracing, the tester prevented elevation of the shoulder, raising the elbow, and abducting the arm.

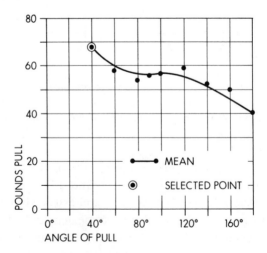

Fig. 2.17   Elbow extension strength curve

The strongest position for this movement was with the elbow fully flexed, when the muscles were on greatest stretch. A plateau occurred from 60 to 140 degrees, followed by some dropping off as the elbow straightened to 180 degrees. The strength means of the subjects ranged from 40 pounds at 180 degrees to 68 pounds at 40 degrees; the mean increase was 28 pounds, or 70 per cent.

Hɪᴘ ᴇxᴛᴇɴsɪᴏɴ (Fig. 2.18). The position for the hip extension strength test was: Subject supine, free leg flexed, with foot resting on table, arms folded on chest; leg being tested adducted at hip joint to 180 degrees (Fig. 2.7B). The tester braced the subject's shoulders and prevented lifting the buttocks.

The greatest strength for this movement was with the hip fully flexed when the muscles were on greatest stretch. A plateau occurred at the end of the movement, which was partly due to the increased weight of the leg which must be lifted as the leg straightens. The strength means of the subjects ranged from 127 pounds at 170 degrees to 186 pounds at 50 degrees; the mean increase was 59 pounds, or 46 per cent.

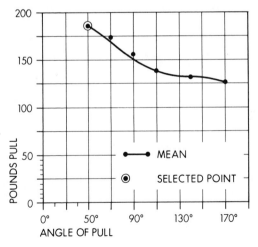

Fig. 2.18 **Hip extension strength curve**

HIP ADDUCTION. The position for the hip adduction strength test was: Subject supine, legs extended at knee and hip joints to 180 degrees, arms folded on chest; the leg being tested was extended at hip joint to 180 degrees (Fig. 2.8 B).

As only three angle positions were used for this movement, a graph was not prepared. The results of the testing were as follows:

Angles	Means (*lbs.*)
135°	106
160°	102
180°	91

The greatest strength for this movement was applied at 135 degrees, with the leg away from the body. However, only a 4-pound reduction occurred at 160 degrees. The drop in strength at 180 degrees was more pronounced. The mean increase from 180 to 135 degrees was 15 pounds, or 17 per cent.

ANKLE PLANTAR FLEXION. The position for the ankle plantar flexion strength test was: Subject supine, legs extended at knee and hip joints to 180 degrees, arms folded on chest (Fig. 2.12B). The body was braced at the shoulders by the tester to prevent sliding on the table; the leg was kept in contact with the table by further bracing at the knee.

A graph was not prepared for this movement, as only three angle positions were used. The results of the testing were as follows:

Angles	Means (*lbs.*)
90°	150
105°	134
125°	118

The strength curve for this movement is nearly a straight line; the drop was approximately 16 pounds for each angle change. The foot held at a right angle made the strongest position for this movement. The mean increase from 125 to 90 degrees was 32 pounds, or 27 per cent.

Ascending-Descending Curves

Four of the joint movements yielded ascending-descending strength curves. The curves started at a low point at one end, rose to a maximum height in the middle, and descended to a low point at the other end. The joint movements are elbow flexion, shoulder extension, shoulder adduction, and knee extension.

ELBOW FLEXION (Fig. 2.19). The position for the elbow flexion strength curve was: Subject supine, legs flexed at knee and hip joints, with feet resting on table, free arm on chest; upper arm on side tested in 180 degrees of extension and abduction at shoulder joint. Bracing was applied by the tester to prevent raising the elbow and adducting the upper arm.

In this joint movement, a plateau existed at the strongest position for application of strength, between 100 and 140 degrees. The lowest

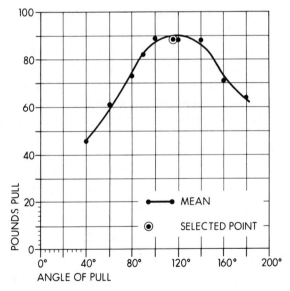

Fig. 2.19   Elbow flexion strength curve

point of strength was at full flexion of the elbow. At complete extension, the muscles are on greatest stretch, but the leverage is poor. The strength means of the subjects ranged from 46 pounds at 40 degrees to 89 pounds at 100 degrees; the increase was 43 pounds, or 94 per cent.

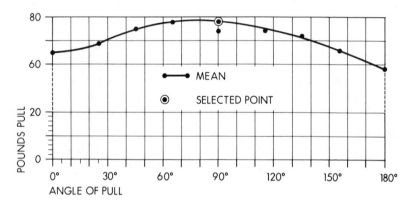

Fig. 2.20   Shoulder extension strength curve

SHOULDER EXTENSION (Fig. 2.20). The position for the shoulder extension strength test was: Subject supine, legs flexed at hip and knee joints, with feet resting on table, free arm on chest; arm being tested adducted at shoulder to 180 degrees. The tester prevented shoulder elevation by bracing, and prevented humerus adduction by guiding with hand.

Only relatively small changes in mean strength occurred throughout this movement. The strength means ranged from 59 pounds at 180 degrees to 78 pounds at 65 degrees; the difference was 19 pounds, or 34 per cent. The variance between 45 and 135 degrees was only 6 pounds, from 72 to 78 pounds.

SHOULDER ADDUCTION (Fig. 2.21). The position for the shoulder adduction strength test was: Subject supine, legs flexed at hip and knee joints, with feet resting on table, free arm on chest; humerus

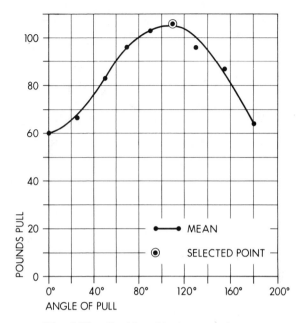

Fig. 2.21 Shoulder adduction strength curve

of arm being tested rotated inward by turning forearm across chest with hand held low toward opposite shoulder (Fig. 2.3).

The graph representing strength for this movement was nearly symmetrical, although a slight plateau between 90 and 110 degrees appeared. Greatest strength was exhibited midway in the range of motion. The shoulder adductors are at a disadvantage when the arm is close to the side of the body, and the weakening of scapular rotators is evident as the arm is pulled from an overhead position. The strength means of the subjects ranged from 60 pounds at 0 degrees to 106 pounds at 110 degrees; the increase was 46 pounds, or 77 per cent.

KNEE EXTENSION (Fig. 2.22). The position for the knee extension strength test was: Subject in sitting position at end of table, free leg hanging free, arms extended backward with hands grasping

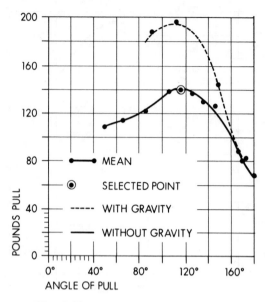

Fig. 2.22   **Knee extension strength curve**

sides of table; thigh of leg being tested adducted at hip to 180 degrees (Fig. 2.10). Lifting of the buttocks and flexion of the elbows were prevented by the tester.

The plateau for this joint movement was from 105 to 125 degrees, the highest part of the strength curve. The lowest point was at full extension, 180 degrees. At the opposite point, full flexion, the muscles were on greatest stretch, but, although they pulled well, they appeared to be at a mechanical disadvantage. The strength means of the subjects ranged from 68 pounds at 180 degrees to 109 pounds at 50 degrees; the increase was 41 pounds, or 60 per cent.

Summary

In this chapter, cable-tension methods, utilizing the tensiometer as the recording instrument, were demonstrated as consistent and valid procedures for the testing of muscle strength. In comparison with the spring scale, the Newman myometer, and the Wakim-Porter strain-gauge device, the tensiometer was found to be the most stable and generally useful of the strength testing instruments.

The chapter presented studies of the body positions best for the application of strength by various joint movements and studies of the muscle strength exerted throughout the full range of joint motion for many of the tests. The following findings were made: other things being equal, a muscle exerts its greatest strength when it functions at its greatest length; the angle at which the muscle pulls is important but probably not so important as its length; the mechanical arrangement of the levers sometimes interferes with the full application of strength, even though the muscles may be at their greatest length; and there appears to be an optimum position at which each muscle functions best in the application of strength.

Chapter **3** / **Ergographic Isotonic Muscular Endurance**

This chapter deals with the evaluation of the volitional isotonic muscular endurance of humans by use of ergographs. As defined in Chapter 1, isotonic muscular endurance is the ability of the muscles to raise and lower a submaximal load; thus, in this work, the muscles alternately shorten and lengthen within the range of motion of a joint and lever system. In this process, degrees of isometric contraction are also encountered in exhaustion performances, especially at the point when fatigued muscles can no longer lift the load through the range of motion but must still maintain a cadence (and, thus, tension) in the test situation. Isometric endurance is defined as *the ability of muscles to maintain maximum static contraction without movement in the joint and lever system.*

Muscular endurance is in a real sense the opposite of muscular fatigue. Karpovich (67) defines fatigue as "decrease in work capacity caused by work itself," and points out that work capacity may also be lowered by other causes such as use of drugs, illness, or lack of incentive. In any event, when fatigued, muscles lose some of their ability to maintain contractile power; this reduction is essentially in proportion to the degree of fatigue imposed on the muscles. This phenomenon is fundamental to the muscular endurance and fatigue studies reported in this chapter. The ergographs utilized in these studies provide the means by which local muscles, or muscles activating particular joint-lever systems, can be isolated and exercised and the work done by them can be measured.

Origins of Ergography

The Italian physiologist, Angelo Mosso of the University of Turin, is credited by Franz (50) with designing the first ergograph, meaning "register of work." Mosso's device (74) was composed of two parts, one of which kept the hand fixed, while the other registered the contractions. This early ergograph consisted of a leather sling which was passed over the finger that was to be exercised. The leather sling was attached to weights by means of a string which passed over a pulley. A record of the performance was made by a pen carried by a small car that was pulled by the string so that it slid along two parallel horizontal steel rods. Thus, when the finger flexed, the car was drawn in one direction, and when the finger flexors relaxed, the weight caused the finger and the car to return to the starting position. In 1900, Franz (50) published exhaustive studies on fatigue in the human muscle which had been conducted by Mosso and his co-workers utilizing the finger ergograph.

The effectiveness of the Mosso ergograph as a device for determining muscular fatigue was criticized by a number of early investigators. Their criticisms were that work was done only during the contractile phase of a rhythmic movement pattern, that the angle of pull changed continuously throughout the range of motion of the joint, that only groups of small muscles capable of moving light loads could be tested, and that no accurate method was available for determining the proper load to be placed on the instrument.

Various modifications of the Mosso finger ergograph were attempted. Franz (50) and Hough (62) introduced spring ergographs to record the tension exerted during isometric contraction, which proved to be no better than the weight ergograph. Hall (55) and Holmes (61) proposed devices to permit work only during the contractile phase of a rhythmic movement pattern. Later, ergographs intended to fatigue larger muscle groups were designed; these included instruments for the muscles activating the elbow joint (86) and for the gripping muscles of the hand (69). However, it was not until 1942 that the ergographs used in the studies reported in this monograph were designed by Kelso from specifications provided by Hellebrandt (59).

The Kelso-Hellebrandt Ergographs

The Kelso-Hellebrandt ergographs were originally designed for disability evaluation in the practice of physical medicine and rehabilitation. Frances A. Hellebrandt, M.D., is a physiatrist and L. E. A. Kelso is a professor of mechanical engineering; thus, the physician and the engineer joined their competencies to devise proper instruments appropriate for the evaluation of injured or handicapped patients. The ergographs were designed to help evaluate the skeletal and neuromuscular systems of the upper extremities, since they participate to a lesser or greater extent in nearly all occupational pursuits. Deformity, injury, or disease affecting the power of the muscles to develop tension or to transmit the tension thus developed to a strong and mobile lever system, reduce man's ability to work. As a consequence of this need, Hellebrandt, Kelso, and associates devised five instruments: finger and wrist ergograph (60), radioulnar ergograph (60), elbow and shoulder ergograph (60), thumb ergograph (58), and grip ergograph (57).

As indicated above, earlier ergographs permitted the angle of pull to change continuously as the body part serving as a lever moved in an arc during isotonic contractions; the component capable of producing rotary movement also varied continuously. Consequently, it was impossible to compute by any simple means the total work done by the contracting muscles. Therefore, Kelso replaced the Mosso sling with a bell crank or wheel and axle. For this arrangement, the body part serving as lever activates an adjustable crank, or lever arm, which is attached to an axle. When the ergographic load is lifted, the wheel turns as the lever arm moves in an arc. Thus, the angle at which resistance is exerted remains constant throughout the full range of movement.

The lifting force for the Kelso-Hellebrandt elbow-shoulder ergograph is transmitted from the bell crank to a power sprocket over a secondary wheel and axle in the tower of the carrier which supports the load; the load moves on a carrier traveling with minimum friction on two vertical rods. For purposes of more objective testing in the present studies, a clamp was placed on the carrier guide rod at a point representing the approximate height of the lift; thus, a stopping point for each lift was clearly defined. Two meters are located in the tower: one of these is a repetition meter, indicating the number of times the load is lifted; the other is a distance meter, providing in centimeters the cumulative height of successive lifts. Provision is made for an ink-writing capillary pen to record the lifts on the drum of a slowly moving kymograph. Time can be recorded in any desired interval by a simple mechanical chronograph driven by a 6 r.p.m. synchronous motor.

In disability evaluation, Hellebrandt, Skowland, and Kelso (60) reported that the number of contractions per bout was dependent upon the condition of the muscle group and the severity of the work desired. Each series of contractions was called a bout and a rest of 60 seconds was allowed between successive bouts. The number of bouts per treatment period also depended upon the patient's condition and the purpose of the exercise. The exercise technician determined the optimum contraction-relaxation rate by trial as that load which is capable of just producing an asymtotic fatigue curve in 25 to 40 repetitions at the selected rhythm. This could be complete or incomplete; that is, the fatigue curve could fall to zero in the required number of contractions or to some fraction of the initial extent of contraction. From 10 to 20 bouts constituted one treatment period.

Adjustments to improvement or regression in the fatigue curves could easily be made by increasing or decreasing the load in accordance with the result desired.

Hellebrandt and associates (58) also introduced a "limit-day" procedure in ergographic exercise, which was patterned after De-Lorne's limit-day technique (48). Repetitive bouts of 10 contractions each with 30-second rest pauses between them were performed against progressively increasing resistance. For the thumb movement, for example, the load increment was .25 kg., added to the ergograph carriage during each 30-second rest pause between bouts. By this process, the load for optimal functional capacity was identified as the load which elicited the greatest amount of work done in one bout of 10 contractions. Any stress beyond this point falls in the overload zone and is thus suitable for exercise aimed at the development of strength.

Single-Bout Elbow Flexion Ergography

Earlier investigators have indicated that single ergographic exercise bouts to exhaustion are unsatisfactory for test purposes, as such testing lacks precision, or satisfactory repeatability of test results. Hellebrandt, Kelso, Houtz, and Eubank (58) stated that this process is satisfactory for exercise and disability evaluation only if the load and rhythm of contraction are so adjusted that the extent of maximum volitional shortening falls off progressively until the resisting weight can no longer be lifted. Choice of the appropriate load and cadence for such ergographic testing, however, was left entirely to a trial and error process. The purpose of this section is to present the results of studies designed to determine procedures for objectively determining work conditions for employing Kelso-Hellebrandt ergographs in single exercise bouts.* While the stated

---

* Acknowledgment is made to L. E. A. Kelso for the construction of the ergographs utilized in these studies and to F. A. Hellebrandt for providing guidance in their use.

purpose is related to instrumentation, other values from this research will follow as a better understanding is acquired of volitional muscle action under conditions of fatigue contraction.

Nonexhaustion Exercise Bouts

Initial ergographic exercise studies were limited to the use of the elbow flexor muscles. Basic to the operation of the ergograph in these and other studies was the belief that the ergograph could be loaded effectively by utilizing weights equal to some proportion of the strength of the muscles to be exercised (to be known hereafter as "strength proportion"). It was anticipated that the strength of the muscles could be measured isometrically by cable-tension methods, as described in Chapter 2. In this way, the load would be individually adapted by using strength proportions, rather than adopting a uniform weight for all subjects.

As a preliminary investigation (20) into strength proportions relative to work output, two factors were studied: (a) the precision with which ergographic testing of the elbow flexor muscles can be accomplished; and (b) the effectiveness of various strength proportions to designate weight loads in the ergographic testing of these muscles.

Instead of permitting each subject to continue until exhaustion was reached, a time limit of two minutes was imposed; this practice was intended to eliminate (or, at least, reduce) psychological factors present in exhaustion testing. Thus, weight loads were sought which permitted the subjects to exercise on the ergograph for this length of time. A set cadence was adopted for all testing; this cadence was 60, or 30 repetitions of raising and lowering the load per minute. Believing that individuals with long arms might be at some disadvantage when exercising on the ergograph, an eight-inch lever arm was used for all subjects. The ergographic testing techniques finally adopted are presented later in this chapter. The subjects were 66 college men.

Under these test conditions, proportions of one-eighth, one-sixth, and one-fourth strength were tried. For one-eighth proportion, all subjects completed the two minutes; for one-sixth proportion, all subjects completed only three-fourths of the time limit; and for one-fourth loads, 60 per cent of the subjects failed to complete the two minutes. Therefore, with one-eighth proportion, the subjects were tested twice; the test-retest correlation based on cumulative distances loads were lifted was .74.

In this preliminary investigation of single-bout ergographic testing of the elbow flexor muscles, various difficulties were encountered which may have caused, in part at least, the rather low test-retest correlation. Among difficulties were the following: (a) Untrained subjects were used. Other experimenters working with ergography have indicated that best results are obtained when the subjects have gone through sufficient instruction and practice sessions to master the techniques and to experience the rigors of strenuous performance. (b) The two tests from which the correlation was computed were given approximately ten minutes apart. Variations in the recovery of the subjects from the first test may account for inconsistencies in results on the second test. (c) The placement of the subject in relation to the ergograph and his stabilization during strenuous effort were not adequately controlled. These difficulties could also logically result in test-retest inconsistencies. In subsequent ergographic testing, efforts were made to improve these situations.

As indicated, a basic problem of ergographic testing was so to control the subjects' movements and their position at the ergograph that repeatable results could be obtained. Consequently, special adjustable braces were designed and constructed, which, when attached to the testing table, held the subject's shoulders and feet in proper position.

With improved testing techniques and by use of the shoulder and foot braces, the precision of ergographic testing of the elbow flexor muscles was studied further. The ergographic weight load for each subject was only sufficient to induce mild to moderate fatigue; in no instance was an exhaustion state reached. Thus, the additional complications encountered in exhaustion efforts continued to be avoided.

For this testing, the amount of weight placed on the ergograph carriage for each subject was one-eighth proportion of his elbow flexion strength; the cadence was 60, as before; and the time limit of two minutes was again imposed. The subjects were 31 college men. Each subject participated in one testing session each week for three weeks. Four test bouts were completed at each session with ten-minute rests between bouts. When the same weight load was maintained for each subject, the test-retest correlations were .90 and above, whether the ergographic tests were given on the same day or on different days.

In order to determine the effect on ergographic performance when using different lengths of lever arms, the subjects were tested in the same manner as above, but with the following three arm lengths: the regular eight-inch length employed so far, a point midway between the elbow and wrist joints of each subject, and with the handle of the lever arm held in the palm of the hand. The coefficients obtained from intercorrelating the results of ergographic testing with these different lengths of lever arms were between .90 and .95.

However, the work done with the different lever arms did vary. Computing work done as weight load in grams times cumulative distance lifted in centimeters, the means were as follows:

Palm of hand	274,130 cm.-gms.
Eight-inch arm	217,976 cm.-gms.
Mid-forearm	195,564 cm.-gms.

For all comparisons, the differences between the means were significant beyond the .01 level; the *t* ratios ranged from 3.37 to 10.23. Thus, while the tester may use any length of lever arm desired, the arms should not be interchanged if test results are to be compared. Whether the same results would occur when the ergographic testing is carried to exhaustion is not known from this experimentation.

The effect of practice and conditioning upon the results of ergographic testing under the above nonexhaustive exercise conditions was checked for the three weeks' testing sessions just described. It is judged that the overload imposed on the subjects was mild to moderate. Although there appeared to be a small but consistent gain in work output for the twelve test bouts, the amount was not significant; the *t* ratio for the difference between the first and last work output means was 1.45.

Exhaustion Exercise Bouts

As indicated above, a high degree of precision for elbow flexion ergographic testing is possible under conditions of mild to moderate muscular fatigue. In Fig. 3.1, kymograph tracings are presented which illustrate ergographic performances where mild to moderate loads were used and a time limit of two minutes was imposed. The subject whose performance is shown in Fig. 3.1A did not show any diminution in the height the load was lifted; in this instance, the load was one-eighth of the strength of his elbow flexor muscles. When the amount of the load was doubled to a one-fourth proportion, the subject depicted had some decrease in the distance he could lift the load during the last 30 seconds of the effort (Figure 3.1B).

Attempts were made next to extend ergographic testing conditions inducing exhaustion, that is, exercise carried to the point where the subject no longer moved his arm enough to activate the ergograph's distance meter (24). As a result of initial exhaustian studies, it became apparent that consistent results in single-bout ergographic muscular fatigue testing could only be achieved when the ergograph loads were such as to induce exhaustion in a relatively short time. Fig. 3.2A illustrates the ergographic performance of a subject when the weight load was one-fourth elbow flexion strength; the subject continued exercising for an indefinite time. In the illustration, the bout continued for 4.5 minutes until finally stopped by the tester. The form of the tracing was erratic, with decreases in the amount of the forearm movement followed by increases. Consistency between test bouts in this situation was impossible.

With ergograph loads of three-eighths proportion, however, a very different kymograph tracing resulted, as shown in Fig. 3.2B.

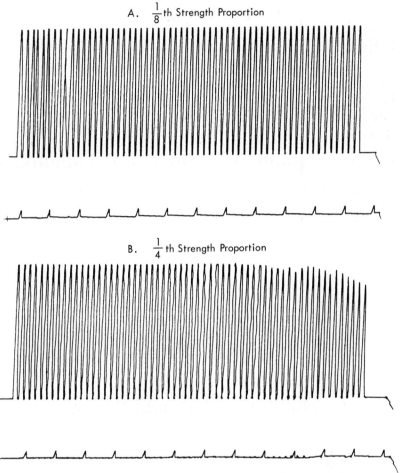

Figs. 3.1A, B Elbow flexion kymograph tracings—2-minute test bouts

In this instance, the decline in the length of forearm movements was smooth; and the amount of time to reach exhaustion was relatively short, less than two minutes.

Based upon this experience, the correlations between repeated tests were computed when the ergograph load for each subject was three-eighths of his elbow flexion strength, the cadence was 60 (or

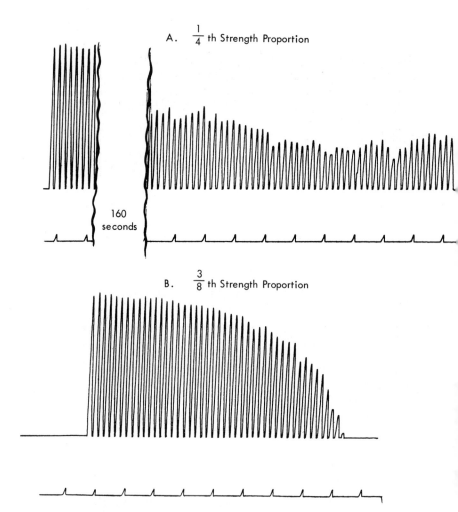

Figs. 3.2A, B Elbow flexion kymograph tracings—unlimited time bouts

30 repetitions per minute), and the bout continued until movement of the forearm became so slight that the ergograph distance meter stopped recording. The subjects were 64 college men. During the first week of this exhaustion testing, two test bouts were administered on the same day with a 30–minute rest period intervening. For two additional weeks, two exhaustion bouts were conducted on

separate days, thus allowing a minimum of 24 hours' rest between bouts.

The test-retest correlations for the six ergographic exercise bouts are given in Table 3.1. The correlation between the bouts given on the same day (1A vs. 1B) was .79. The correlations between the first bout of the first week (1A) and the other bouts ranged from .75 to .82, all but one, however, being below .80. Thus, the correlation between the two bouts on the same day with a 30-minute rest between them proved to be as high as between those administered on separate days with the initial test. As time progressed and ergographic testing experience was gained, however, the magnitude of the test-retest correlations increased. All but one of the correlations during the second and third weeks were in the .80's; three of the six correlations were either .84 or .85. Inasmuch as a significant muscle-conditioning effect was subsequently found to be produced by repeated exhaustion bouts and was not taken into account in this situation, the precision results from this form of testing were considered satisfactory. Subsequently, test-retest correlations of .85 were also obtained without the use of braces in exhaustion testing.

Table 3.1

CORRELATIONS BETWEEN SINGLE-BOUT ELBOW FLEXION
ERGOGRAPHY UNDER CONDITIONS OF
EXHAUSTION TESTING

Test Bouts	r	Test Bouts	r
*1A vs. 1B	.79	2A vs. 2B	.84
1A vs. 2A	.76	2A vs. 3A	.75
1A vs. 2B	.75	2A vs. 3B	.82
1A vs. 3A	.82	2B vs. 3A	.85
1A vs. 3B	.75	2B vs. 3B	.84
		3A vs. 3B	.80

*The numeral designates the week; the letter, the test bout each week. Thus, 3B indicates third week, second bout.

Linearity

An inspection of scattergrams for the various test-retest correlations between the exhaustion bouts just reported seemed to indicate possible currilinearity in the arrangements of the paired scores. As a consequence, etas were computed for both regression lines of each correlation. These etas showed increases in magnitude over the linear *r*'s, especially during the second and third weeks. All but one eta reached or exceeded .80; when confined to testing during the second and third weeks, seven etas reached or exceeded .90.

Some risk, however, is encountered in applying eta to correlations when the number of subjects is small, as in this research (65). When these etas were corrected for N and the number of arrays, their magnitude was reduced. When the differences between the *r*'s and the corrected etas were tested for currilinearity by application of chi-square, none proved to be significant. As a consequence, no claim for such linearity is made for these data. Possibly, subsequent research with a larger number of subjects may produce results that are more conclusive in this respect. The rationale supporting a currilinear hypothesis is the presence of muscular conditioning from repeated ergographic exercise bouts.

Testing Techniques

As finally devised, the techniques of ergographic testing of the elbow flexor muscles of the left arm are described below.

1. Prior to ergographic testing, administer elbow flexion strength test. This testing technique is based on cable-tension methods utilizing a tensiometer, and is as follows (Fig. 3.3):

STARTING POSITION. (a) Subject in supine position, hips and knees flexed comfortably; free hand resting on chest. (b) Upper arm on side tested close to side; elbow in 115 degrees flexion; forearm in mid-prone-supine position.

ATTACHMENTS. (a) Regulation strap placed around forearm midway between wrist and elbow joint. (b) Pulling assembly hooked toward subject's feet on table runner.

PRECAUTIONS. (a) Prevent raising of elbow and abducting of shoulder by bracing elbow. (b) Stabilize subject on table by bracing legs.

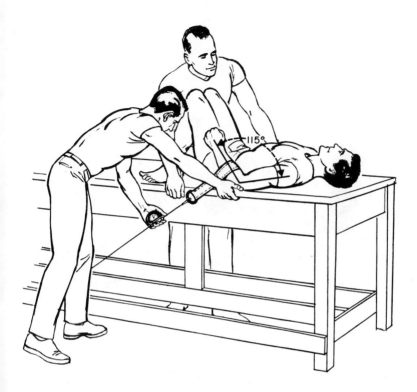

Fig. 3.3   **Elbow flexion strength**

2. Place load equal to three-eighths of subject's elbow flexion strength on ergograph carriage.

3. Arrange subject's body in same position as for strength test, shoulder and feet against their respective braces; center of elbow joint located opposite bell-crank shaft of ergograph; fasten cuff* at end of eight-inch lever arm firmly to subject's left forearm. (Fig. 3.4)

4. Permit two or three preliminary lifts. Then record numbers on the repetition counter and cumulative-distance meter; attach

---

* A specially devised felt cuff, or an archery arm guard, lined with a quarter-inch sponge-rubber pad for comfort, can be used for this purpose.

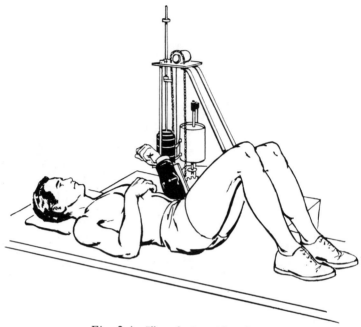

Fig. 3.4 **Elbow flexion without brace**

kymograph if recording is to be made. Start metronome set for one-second movements.

5. Allow subject to begin test bout when ready in cadence with metronome. Stress necessity for maintaining cadence even though subject is unable to make full flexion movements as test bout continues.

6. Read repetition counter and distance meter immediately after completion of test.

Shoulder Flexion Ergography

In Chapter 2, the amounts of muscular strength that can be applied at different points throughout the range of motion of various joints of the body were noted. As shown in Fig. 2.19, the strongest position for elbow flexion was midway in the range of motion, between 100 and 140 degrees, with a decrease of approximately 28 per cent as the forearm was extended to 180 degrees. Thus, in ergographic exercise, each lift is initiated at a weak strength position, and, as exhaustion is approached, the elbow movement is more and more limited to this weak muscular zone.

As a consequence of this observation, an investigation was made of the effect upon ergographic testing when the joint is in the strongest position at the point of exhaustion (24). The shoulder flexion movement was selected, as in this movement greatest strength is achieved at 180 degrees, with arm parallel to the side of the body; the curve of strength for this movement was shown in Fig. 2.15.

The position of the body for shoulder flexion ergographic exercise procedure was similar to the position for elbow flexion ergography, except that the center of the shoulder joint was located opposite the bell-crank shaft and the bracing assembly was not used. The cadence was maintained at 60, as before.

Test bouts with two-minute time limits were given again for ergographic loads based on various strength proportions. When ergographic exercises with loads equal to one-eighth of shoulder flexion strength were given twice, 10 minutes apart, the correlation between the tests was .98; nearly all subjects exactly repeated their performances each time. Comparable results occurred when the ergographic load was one-fourth shoulder flexion strength. And again, when three-eighths proportion was used, the proportion that resulted in exhaustion of elbow flexor muscles in less than two minutes, the ergographic exercise continued mostly with full lifts for the entire time. For the most part, under all three conditions, the kymograph tracings were true rectangles, indicating that the fatigue effects of these amounts of exercise was not sufficient to decrease the distance the load could be lifted.

In exhaustion ergographic testing, the subjects performed exercise test bouts with three different proportions of their shoulder flexion strength, one-fourth, three-eighths, and five-eighths; the results are illustrated in the kymograph tracings in Fig. 3.5. When a one-fourth proportion was used, the subjects exercised for long pe-

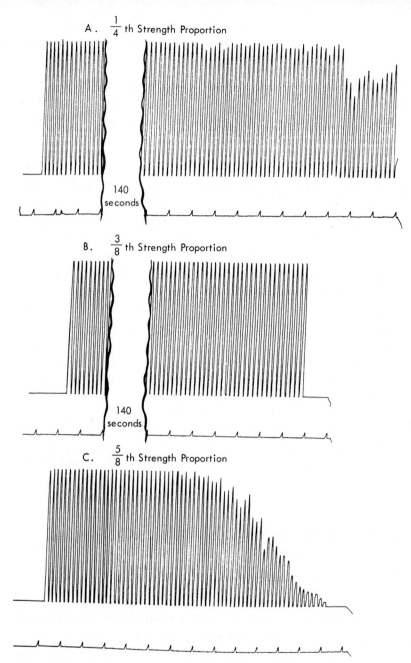

Figs. 3.5A, B, C   Shoulder flexion kymograph tracings—unlimited time bouts

riods of time, in some instances for half an hour and more. The kymograph tracing (Fig. 3.5A) illustrates this situation. The subject was stopped just short of five minutes; fatigue was noticeable at the end of this time, but the performance was erratic. Similar results were obtained when the ergograph weight was increased to three-eighths proportion (Fig. 3.5B). Ergographic testing precision under these conditions was not possible.

Finally, the ergograph load was increased to five-eighths proportion of each subject's shoulder flexion strength. This amount proved sufficient to induce exhaustion in a reasonable length of time. The kymograph tracing (Fig. 3.5C) shows a rectangle for the first minute, followed by a consistent decline to exhaustion in the next 70 seconds. The correlation between repeated test bouts with this strength proportion given on separate days was .85.

The greater proportion of strength required for the shoulder flexion movement, as contrasted with the elbow flexion movement, is attributed to the fact that the muscles are able to exert their greatest strength at the point of greatest stress in ergographic testing. This point is with the shoulder extended in the shoulder flexion test and is midway through the elbow movement in the elbow flexion test.

Optimum Work Output

In the ergographic studies reported so far in this chapter, it was demonstrated that the amount of weight to be used for each subject could be effectively determined as a proportion of the strength of the muscles to be exercised. With an eight-inch ergograph lever arm and with a cadence of 60, or 30 repetitions per minute, proportions found to be satisfactory were: three-eighths of maximum elbow flexion strength for elbow flexion ergography and five-eighths of maximum shoulder flexion strength for shoulder flexion ergography. These studies did not determine the conditions for optimum work output. Consequently, investigations were undertaken to ascertain such conditions for elbow flexion, elbow extension, shoulder flexion, and grip ergography.

General Procedures

The Kelso-Hellebrandt elbow and shoulder ergograph was utilized for all movements except for gripping. The grip ergograph (Fig. 3.6) is fundamentally the same as the other Kelso-Hellebrandt ergographs (57). However, the force applied by the gripping muscles is transmitted through a hydraulic system instead of a sprocket wheel and lever arm. A bulb is attached to a rubber hose, which is connected to two sylphon-type valve tops with a pressure gauge between them. The two valves allow water to be forced into the closed system and permit air to be released. When the bulb is compressed, the sylphon bellows are filled and a rod through the base of the larger inverted valve top rises, thus moving a lever system provided with an

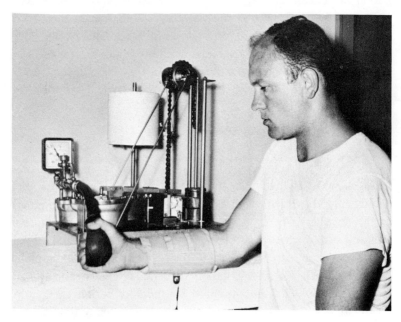

Fig. 3.6   Grip ergograph testing

adjustable fulcrum. The load is raised by the connecting bicycle chain.

For each of the four movements (that is, elbow flexion, elbow extension, shoulder flexion, and gripping), 25 different combinations of load and cadence were studied; for each combination, five subjects were used, thus necessitating 125 subjects for each movement. These subjects were randomly selected male students at the University of Oregon between the ages of 18 and 26 years, who were free of physical handicaps. A table of random numbers was utilized to assign subjects to the 25 conditions.

The statistical analysis employed in these studies consisted of comparison of mean work outputs (load in kilograms times cumulative distance in centimeters). For each movement, the differences between the highest mean and other high means were tested for significances by application of the t ratio. With 8 degrees of freedom ($N_1 + N_2 - 2$, or $5 + 5 - 2 = 8$), a t ratio of 2.31 is necessary for a significant difference at the .05 level.

When significance was not achieved for a single combination of load and cadence, 11 additional subjects were tested for each condition with relatively high mean work output. The number thus became 16 and the degrees of freedom became 30 for each difference between means to be tested; the t ratio for significance at the .05 level is 2.04.

Elbow Flexion Conditions

All combinations of the following five loads and five cadences were chosen to determine optimum work output for elbow flexion ergography (34):

Loads: The loads were proportions in kilograms of elbow flexion strength, as follows: 1/8, 3/16, 1/4, 5/16, and 3/8.

Cadences: The cadences on the metronome were: 44, 60, 76, 92, and 108. The numbers of repetitions per minute were one-half of these cadences, as the cadences provided for raising and lowering the load.

Subjects included in this part of the study were limited to these with elbow flexion strength between 85 and 128 pounds, roughly the middle 80 per cent of subjects available. This restriction was necessary as ergograph weights were not sufficient to provide for subjects with strength beyond 128 pounds when the heaviest load was used; a comparable limitation was placed on subjects with the lowest scores, thus eliminating the upper and lower 10 per cent. The exercise bout for each subject continued for two minutes or until he reached volitional exhaustion. The position for exercising on the ergograph was the same as described earlier in this chapter.

The work output means obtained for the 25 combinations of loads and cadences appear in Table 3.2. The greatest mean outputs were as follows: 20,352 cm.-kg. for one-fourth proportion at 76 cadence (condition 13), 18,934 cm.-kg. for one-eighth proportion at 108 cadence (condition 21), and 18,142 cm.-kg. for one-fourth proportion at 92 cadence (condition 18). The differences between the mean of condition 13 and the means of conditions 21 and 18 were 1,418 and 2,210 cm.-kg. respectively; the corresponding t ratios were 1.47 and 2.63. Thus, the difference between the work output means for conditions 13 and 18 exceeded significance at the .05 level.

In order to test further the difference in mean work output be-

Table 3.2

ELBOW FLEXION ERGOGRAPHY: MEAN WORK OUTPUTS (Cm.-Kg.)*
FOR VARYING CONDITIONS OF LOADS AND CADENCES†

Cadence	Weight Loads: Proportions of Strength				
	1/8	3/16	1/4	5/16	3/8
44	8,583 (1)	12,806 (2)	15,504 (3)	16,791 (4)	16,538 (5)
60	12,622 (6)	17,815 (7)	17,837 (8)	16,793 (9)	14,265 (10)
76	15,951 (11)	17,223 (12)	20,352 (13)	14,522 (14)	15,401 (15)
92	15,951 (16)	16,281 (17)	18,142 (18)	16,535 (19)	15,948 (20)
108	18,934 (21)	16,643 (22)	17,724 (23)	17,032 (24)	16,285 (25)

* Time limit of two minutes imposed on all bouts.
† Condition numbers are in parentheses. $N = 5$

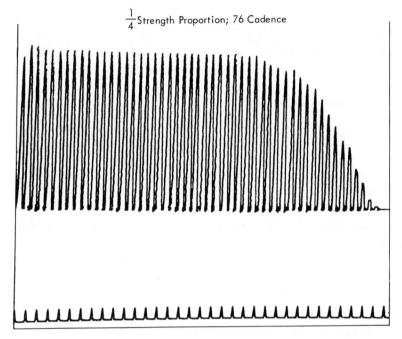

$\frac{1}{4}$Strength Proportion; 76 Cadence

Figs. 3.7   **Kymograph tracing for elbow flexion ergographic exercise
to exhaustion**

tween conditions 13 and 21, 11 more subjects were tested for each
condition. As a result of this additional testing, the two means were
reduced somewhat; the means were 18,681 and 16,222 cm.-kg. with
condition 13 maintaining superiority. The difference between the
means was 2,459 cm.-kg.; the *t* ratio was 1.98, which nearly reached
significance at the .05 level.

Judging from the results of this study, single-bout elbow flexion
ergographic testing should be done with a load of one-fourth proportion of elbow flexion strength and a cadence of 76. Under this
condition, the mean work output was greatest, although significant superiority was not adequately demonstrated over the condition of one-
eighth proportion at 108 cadence. A kymograph tracing illustrating
the chosen condition appears in Fig. 3.7. This subject maintained

complete lifts of the ergograph load for 33 contractions; during the next 32 lifts, his performance dropped rapidly until he no longer moved the load. The over-all time for the subject in the illustration was 102 seconds. The test-retest correlation for this condition was .87.

Shoulder Flexion Conditions

After exploratory trials, the weight loads and cadences selected for shoulder flexion ergography (34) were as follows:

LOADS. The loads were proportions in kilograms of shoulder flexion strength, as follows: 1/2, 9/16, 5/8, 11/16, and 3/4.

CADENCES. The cadences on the metronome were: 52, 60, 68, 76, and 84. The numbers of repetitions per minute were one-half of these cadences, as the cadences provided for raising and lowering the load.

The same two-minute time limitation as for elbow flexion ergography was imposed. The position for exercising on the ergograph was the same as previously described in this chapter.

Table 3.3

SHOULDER FLEXION ERGOGRAPHY: MEAN WORK OUTPUTS (Cm.-Kg.)*
FOR VARYING CONDITIONS OF LOADS AND CADENCES†

Cadence	*Weight Loads: Proportions of Strength*				
	1/2	*9/16*	*5/8*	*11/16*	*3/4*
52	20,985 (1)	22,162 (2)	19,492 (3)	20,174 (4)	19,035 (5)
60	24,001 (6)	24,349 (7)	21,912 (8)	22,102 (9)	17,359 (10)
68	22,006 (11)	19,766 (12)	16,454 (13)	21,614 (14)	20,942 (15)
76	20,687 (16)	21,843 (17)	22,277 (18)	18,051 (19)	19,802 (20)
84	20,666 (21)	25,325 (22)	20,053 (23)	21,697 (24)	25,181 (25)

* Time limit of two minutes imposed on all bouts.
† Condition numbers are in parentheses.   N = 5

The work output means obtained for the 25 combinations of load and cadence appear in Table 3.3. The greatest mean outputs were as follows: 25,325 cm.-kg. for nine-sixteenths proportion at 84 cadence (condition 22), 25,181 cm.-kg. for three-fourths proportion at 84 cadence (condition 25), 24,349 cm.-kg. for nine-sixteenths proportion at 60 cadence (condition 7), 24,001 cm.-kg. for one-half proportion at 60 cadence (condition 6), and 22,277 cm.-kg. for five-eighths proportion at 76 cadence (condition 18). The differences between the highest mean, condition 22, and the other means ranged from 144 to 2,058 cm.-kg. None of these differences was significant; the highest *t* ratio was .70.

Consequently, 11 more subjects were tested for each of these five conditions. As a result of this additional testing, the five means were reduced considerably, the reductions ranging from 3,271 to

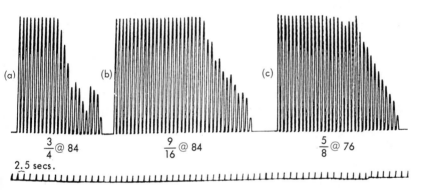

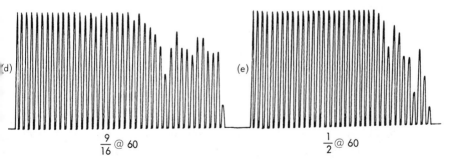

Fig. 3.8A, B, C, D, E

4,636 cm.-kg.; the highest mean (condition 25) was 21,199 cm.-kg. The differences between the means were greater than for five subjects, ranging from 445 to 2,192 cm.-kg.; the *t* ratios were also higher, between .50 and 1.16. Thus, the differences between the means did not reach the .05 level of significance.

For shoulder flexion ergography, the combination of three-fourths proportion of shoulder flexion strength and a cadence of 84 had the highest mean. However, as this advantage was not significant, other methods could be justified for this form of testing. The kymograph tracings for the five highest conditions are presented in Fig. 3.8; as these represent performances of five different subjects, individual differences are incorporated in the illustrations, so the results may only be compared generally. Performances with the faster cadences of 76 and 84 resulted in shorter work bouts despite equivalent work done; the times required for these exhaustion tests were 35, 60, and 48 seconds for 3.8 A-B-C, in that order. For the slower cadence of 60, the times required to reach exhaustion in the performances shown were 75 and 85 seconds for 3.8 D and E, respectively. All performances were considerably shorter than the two minutes imposed on all exercise sessions.

Gripping Conditions

Preliminary trials of various weights and cadences were conducted with a few subjects on the grip ergograph (34). On this basis, the following were selected:

LOADS. The loads were proportions in kilograms of grip strength, as follows: 1/8, 1/4, 3/8, 1/2, and 5/8. Grip strength was tested by squeezing a manuometer as hard as possible, in accordance with the technique described by Clarke (14).

CADENCES. The cadences on the metronome were: 44, 52, 60, 68, and 76. The numbers of repetitions per minute were one-half of these cadences, as the cadences provided for raising and lowering the load.

The position for exercising on the grip ergograph is illustrated in Fig. 3.6. The subject sat beside the test table holding the ergograph bulb. An arm guard was strapped to his forearm and attached to the table in order to stabilize the exercising arm. The usual two-minute time limit was placed on this testing.

The work output means obtained for 25 combinations of loads and cadences appear in Table 3.4. Inasmuch as high means resulted from testing with the highest cadence, 76, five subjects were tested for each of three additional conditions, cadence 84 with one-fourth, three-eighths, and one-half proportions. These results are also included in Table 3.4.

Table 3.4

GRIP ERGOGRAPHY: MEAN WORK OUTPUTS (Cm.-Kg.)*
FOR VARYING CONDITIONS OF LOADS AND CADENCES†

| | *Weight Loads: Proportions of Strength* | | | | |
Cadence	*1/8*	*1/4*	*3/8*	*1/2*	*5/8*
44	3,463 (1)	6,913 (2)	7,860 (3)	8,449 (4)	8,557 (5)
52	4,248 (6)	7,738 (7)	8,067 (8)	10,577 (9)	6,749 (10)
60	5,058 (11)	9,058 (12)	11,414 (13)	9,610 (14)	8,450 (15)
68	5,026 (16)	9,884 (17)	12,990 (18)	11,665 (19)	7,854 (20)
76	5,723 (21)	10,749 (22)	11,745 (23)	14,749 (24)	8,652 (25)
84		10,751 (26)	8,532 (27)	7,829 (28)	

* Time limit of two minutes imposed on all bouts.
† Condition numbers are in parentheses.   N = 5

The greatest mean work outputs for this testing were as follows: 14,749 cm.-kg. for one-half proportion at 76 cadence (condition 24), 12,990 cm.-kg. for three-eighths proportion at 68 cadence (condition 18), and 11,745 cm.-kg. for three-eights proportion at 76 cadence (condition 23). The differences between the mean of condition 24 and the means of conditions 18 and 23 were 1,759 and 3,004 cm.-kg. respectively. These differences were not significant at the .05 level, since the corresponding *t* ratios were 1.52 and 1.72.

As was done for the other movements, 11 more subjects were tested for each of the three conditions with highest means. From this testing, the mean work output for condition 24 became 15,649 cm.-kg., an increase of 900 cm.-kg. The means for conditions 18 and 23 also increased but not as much, 532 and 37 cm.-kg. respectively. The differences between the means of conditions 24 and 18 was 3,191 cm.-kg.; and between the means of conditions 24 and 23, 3,941 cm.-kg. These differences were significant well beyond the .05 level, since the corresponding t ratios were 4.28 and 4.61.

For grip ergography, the combination of one-half proportion of grip strength and a cadence of 76 had definite superiority. Consequently, this combination should be used for this form of ergography.

Elbow Extension Conditions

Preliminary trials of various weights and cadences were made on the elbow extension ergograph (80). On this basis, the following were selected.

LOADS. The loads were proportions in kilograms of elbow extension strength, as follows: 7/16, 1/2, 9/16, 5/8, and 11/16. Elbow extension strength was tested by cable-tension methods, as described by Clarke and Clarke (28).

CADENCES. The cadences on the metronome were 52, 60, 68, 76, and 84. The numbers of repetitions per minute were one-half of these cadences, as the cadences provided for raising and lowering the load.

The position of the subject for elbow extension ergographic testing was the same as for the elbow flexion movement. As for the other ergographic tests, a two-minute time limit was imposed.

The work output means obtained for the 25 combinations of loads and cadences appear in Table 3.5. The greatest mean outputs were as follows: 15,513 cm.-kg. for one-half proportion at 60 cadence (condition 7), 15,277 cm.-kg. for five-eighths proportion at 52 cadence (condition 4), 15,186 cm.-kg. for one-half proportion at 84 cadence (condition 22), and 14,953 cm.-kg. for seven-sixteenths proportion at 52 cadence (condition 1). The differences between the highest mean (condition 7) and the other means were slight, ranging from

236 to 560 cm.-kg. None of these differences was significant; the highest *t* ratio was .13.

As before, 11 more subjects were tested for each of these five conditions. The differences between the means were greater, but significant differences were not obtained. The highest *t* ratio was 1.06, representing the difference between the work output means of conditions 22 and 7.

Table 3.5

ELBOW EXTENSION ERGOGRAPHY: MEAN WORK OUTPUTS (Cm.-Kg.)*
FOR VARYING CONDITIONS OF LOADS AND CADENCES†

	Weight Loads: Proportions of Strength				
Cadence	7/16	1/2	9/16	5/8	11/16
52	14,953 (1)	13,706 (2)	13,569 (3)	15,277 (4)	10,640 (5)
60	11,265 (6)	15,513 (7)	11,302 (8)	12,298 (9)	13,687 (10)
68	13,839‡ (11)	11,366 (12)	10,316 (13)	7,917‡ (14)	12,118 (15)
76	10,905 (16)	11,418 (17)	11,703 (18)	13,239 (19)	11,114 (20)
84	11,643 (21)	15,186‡ (22)	12,947 (23)	9,193 (24)	11,151 (25)

* Time limits of two minutes imposed on all bouts.
† Condition numbers are in parentheses.   N = 5
‡ Illustrated inconsistent means.   N = 5

For elbow extension ergography, inconsistencies were found in the pattern of work output means for the 25 conditions studied, as can be seen in Table 3.5. Further, superiority was not clearly demonstrated among the four conditions with highest means. Kymograph tracings illustrating performances under these conditions appear in Fig. 3.9; as these represent performances of four different subjects, individual differences are incorporated in the illustrations, so the performances may only be compared generally. The slower cadences of 52 and 60 required the longest time for completion of the exercise bouts (Fig. 3.9B-C-D); for the subjects portrayed, the times ranged between 63 and 70 seconds. When the rapid cadence of 84 was utilized (Fig. 3.9A), the exercise bout lasted only 35 seconds; this time was one-half the time for the same load (one-half proportion) when the cadence was 60.

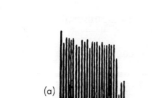
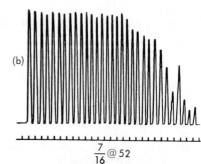

(a)

2.5 sec.

$\frac{1}{2}$@ 84

(b)

$\frac{7}{16}$@ 52

(c)

$\frac{5}{8}$@ 52

(d)

$\frac{1}{2}$@ 60

Fig. 3.9A, B, C, D   Kymograph tracings of elbow extension ergographic exercise patterns for the various strength proportions and cadences

Conditioning Effects from Ergographic Exercise

As indicated earlier in this chapter, even with a limited number of exhaustive bouts, the training effect, as determined by the increased cumulative distance the ergograph load was lifted, was definite and positive. This result was initially observed during the basic studies of ergographic precision testing and of ergographic loading to obtain maximum work output. Consequently, a more systematic approach to the conditioning effects of repeated ergographic exercise bouts was attempted (37). The purpose of this investigation was to determine changes in strength and endurance of the involved muscles as a result of a regimen of single-bout elbow flexion ergographic exercise.

Actually, this experiment was conducted twice. In Experiment A, the number of subjects tested each time varied from 22 to 25; a constant N was not maintained, so that the effects of inconsistencies thus introduced are not known. In Experiment B, the same subjects were tested throughout the study. In both experiments, the subjects were college men without physical handicaps. Results from Experiment B will be reported here, and some comparisons made with the achievements of the former group.

Cable-tension strength tests and ergographic endurance tests of the elbow flexor muscles of the left arm were administered to the 28 subjects three times a week (Monday, Wednesday, and Friday) for four weeks; similar tests were given following a lay-off of four weeks. In addition, the elbow flexor muscles of the right arm were tested on the first and last days of the four-week period, to determine whether any cross transference of conditioning factors to the unexercised arm occurred.

The ergographic exercise specifications required a load equal to three-eighths of each subject's elbow flexion strength and a cadence of 60, or 30 repetitions per minute. Each subject participated in only one such exercise bout carried to exhaustion at each exercise period. Initial ergograph loads were maintained throughout the study. In reporting the results, the test bouts are designated by numeral and letter; the numeral refers to the week and the letter refers to the bout each week. Thus, 3B specifies the second bout of the third week. Bout 1A was a practice bout and is, therefore, omitted.

The statistical treatment of these data consisted of testing the differences between means for significance by application of the *t* ratio. The standard error formula for the difference between means of correlated groups was used, since the study was a single-group experiment. A one-tail significance test was applied, since it was hypothesized that conditioning would take place in one direction only; that is, the exercise effect, if any, would be to condition, not decondition, the muscles. For the one-tail test (27 degrees of freedom), a t ratio of 2.48 is needed for significance at the .01 level.

Muscular Endurance Changes

Evidence of changes in muscular endurance was derived from the cumulative distances the subjects lifted the ergograph loads during each exhaustion bout. The mean distances the subjects achieved each day of the study were graphed, as shown in Fig. 3.10. These results may be summarized as follows:

1. During the first week of the study, no increase in the endurance of the elbow flexor muscles was found. For the next two weeks, the gain was consistent and pronounced. Two gains between successive bouts were significant near or beyond the .01 level; the t ratios for the differences between the means of bouts 2A and 2B and of bouts 2C and 3A were 2.70 and 2.38, respectively. Beginning with bout 3C, a decrease in ergographic distance was recorded, which

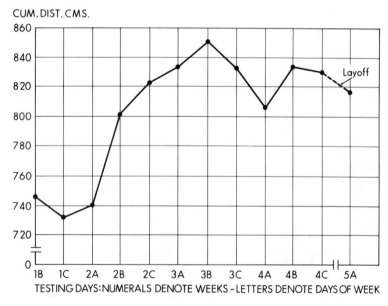

Fig. 3.10 Mean distance in centimeters ergographic loads were moved during elbow flexion exhaustion bouts

continued for two days. On the following test day, a significant gain was recorded; the *t* ratio for the difference between means 4A and 4B was 2.70. These results are similar to those obtained in Experiment A, except that in the earlier study an increase to a greater peak of endurance followed the drop at the end of the third week.

2. The differences between the mean cumulative distances of the first bout (1B) and the subsequent first bouts each week (2A, 3A, and 4A) and the final bout prior to the ergographic exercise lay-off (4C) are shown in Table 3.6. With the exception of the first week, the mean cumulative distance increases were significant at the .01 level and beyond.

Table 3.6

DIFFERENCES BETWEEN MEAN CUMULATIVE DISTANCES
LOADS LIFTED (Cm.) FOR FIRST WEEK AND
SUBSEQUENT WEEKS FOR ELBOW
FLEXION ERGOGRAPHY

Bouts	*Means*	*Mean Difference*	*t Ratio*
1B vs. 2A	745 − 740	− 5	0.25
1B vs. 3A	745 − 836	91	4.55
1B vs. 4A	745 − 808	63	2.86
1B vs. 4C	745 − 818	73	2.92

3. For the basic four weeks of the experiment, which consisted of eleven exercise sessions, the maximum cumulative distance mean achieved by the subjects was 852 cm. for bout 3B; this was a mean gain of 107 cms., or 13 per cent, over the initial mean of 745 cm. For the Experiment A data, this gain was much greater, 34 per cent, at the end of the fourth week.

4. Following the exercise lay-off of four weeks, there was little change in the mean cumulative distance the ergograph loads were lifted (5A). This result was in general accord with other trials of this nature, indicating slight if any muscular endurance deconditioning following cessation of ergographic exercise for this length of time.

5. While the mean scores of the subjects in the experiment indicate changes in the general performance of the group as a whole,

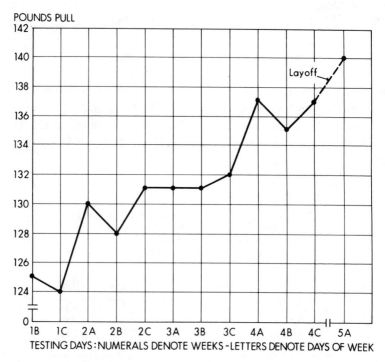

Fig. 3.11 Mean strength in pounds pull of elbow flexion muscles due to exhaustion bouts with these muscles

they do not reveal the muscular endurance conditioning pattern of individual subjects. Believing that such patterns might provide illuminating information relative to the study of muscle conditioning problems, six subjects were selected at random and their cumulative distance scores were plotted for the four weeks of the study. These graph lines showed many individual differences, although all had definite over-all increases. The performance lines of some subjects were more erratic than others, but all revealed a succession of increases and decreases.

Muscular Strength Changes

The muscular strength changes resulting from this experimental procedure were determined from the strength tests of the elbow flexor muscles administered to the subjects each test day prior to exercising on the ergograph. The mean strength scores of the subjects for each day of the study were graphed, as shown in Fig. 3.11. These results may be summarized as follows:

1. During the first week of the study, the elbow flexion strength means dropped slightly. For the next three weeks, a consistent rise occurred, although there were minor drops of one to two pounds, none of which was significant. Two of the successive mean increases were significant at and beyond the .01 level; the *t* ratios for the differences between the means of bouts 1C and 2A and of bouts 3C and 4A were 3.00 and 2.53, respectively. A gain of only two pounds occurred for a period of two weeks (2A to 3C).

2. The differences between the elbow flexion strength mean for the first bout (1B) and subsequent first bouts each week (2A, 3A, and 4A) and the final bout before the exercise lay-off (4C) appear in Table 3.7. All mean increases were significant at and beyond the .01 level; the *t* ratios ranged from 2.5 to 6.0.

Table 3.7

DIFFERENCES BETWEEN STRENGTH TEST MEANS (Lbs.)
FOR FIRST WEEK AND SUBSEQUENT WEEKS
OF ELBOW FLEXION ERGOGRAPHY

Bouts	*Means*	*Mean Difference*	*t Ratio*
1B vs. 2A	125 — 130	5	2.5
1B vs. 3A	125 — 131	6	3.0
1B vs. 4A	125 — 137	12	6.0
1B vs. 4C	125 — 137	12	6.0

3. The over-all increase in mean strength of the elbow flexor muscles for the basic four weeks of the experiment was 12 pounds. The total mean strength gain, therefore, was 10 per cent; for Experiment A, the mean gain was 11 per cent.

4. After the four-week lay-off, muscular strength continued to increase. The strength mean was 139 for test day 5A, a gain of three pounds, which was not significant at the .01 level (t ratio of 1.5). Thus, no deconditioning effect on muscular strength was evident. Similar results occurred in Experiment A.

5. As for the muscular endurance conditioning factor, erratic variations in strength development were found among the six randomly selected subjects. In fact, three of these subjects failed to make an over-all gain in elbow flexion strength.

Cross Transference

A check on the cross transference of the muscular conditioning elements was made by testing the endurance and the strength of the elbow flexor muscles of the unexercised arm at the beginning and end of the four basic weeks of the experiment. While the mean distance the ergograph load was moved was greater, the difference between the means was not significant; the t ratio was .79.

However, in strength, the unexercised arm gained as much as did the exercised arm. The beginning and ending means were 127 and 140 pounds; thus, the difference between means was 13 pounds. This difference was significant well beyond the .01 level since the t ratio was 6.5.

Conclusions

The conditioning effects of ergographic exercise of the elbow flexor muscles, as reflected by changes in their strength and endurance, should be interpreted only in terms of the experimental conditions imposed. Thus: the ergograph weight loads were equal to three-eighths proportion of the strength of each subject's elbow flexor muscles; the cadence was 60, or 30 repetitions per minute; and exercise continued to volitional exhaustion. As a consequence, the subjects exercised from one and one-half to two and one-half minutes each time; the average total length of time the subjects actually exercised on the ergograph during the basic four weeks of the experiment was estimated at 20 to 25 minutes. Under these experimental conditions, then, the following conclusions may be drawn:

1. No increase in muscular endurance was found during the first week of the study; during the next two weeks, there was a steady climb, followed during the fourth week by losses and gains. The over-all gain was 13 per cent; for an earlier experiment (A), this gain was 34 per cent.

2. Beginning with the third test day, there was a generally constant rise in muscular strength throughout the balance of the time. The over-all gain was 10 per cent, which approximated the gain for Experiment A (11 per cent).

3. No appreciable deconditioning in muscular strength and muscular endurance took place after a four-week lay-off from ergographic exercise. Similar results were obtained in the earlier study.

4. In studying the cross transference of conditioning elements from the exercised to the nonexercised arm, no mean gain was found for muscular endurance. However, the mean gain in strength was approximately the same as for the exercised arm.

Summary

In this chapter, the origins of ergography as a means of muscular endurance testing were briefly mentioned and the development of the Kelso-Hellebrandt ergographs, the instruments used in the studies described, was presented. The studies described here established the fact that loading the ergograph for single-bout tests to volitional exhaustion could be accomplished effectively by taking a proportion of the strength of the muscles to be exercised.

Initially, nonexhaustive ergographic exercise bouts of the elbow flexor muscles were undertaken. With loads that permitted the subjects to continue exercising for two minutes, test-retest correlations of between .90 and .95 were obtained. Some difficulty was initially encountered in obtaining testing consistency under conditions of volitional exhaustion performances. Eventually, the test-retest correlations for the various ergographs were established at around .85. With exhaustion testing, however, conditioning of the exercising muscles occurred, as revealed by significantly increased strength and endurance means. Further, individual differences in conditioning occurred, which would tend to lower test-retest correlations.

Loads for effective ergographic testing required a greater proportion of strength when the exercise movement was initiated from a strong strength position. Thus, the work output of muscles is greater when they are in position to apply greatest tension at the point of greatest stress.

The ergographic conditions of load and cadence for optimum work output were studied for four movements: elbow flexion, shoulder flexion, hand grip, and elbow extension. In general, it was found that the speed of muscular contraction affects muscular endurance performance; there appears to be a specific combination or combinations of load and cadence which produces maximum work output of each muscle group.

Finally, in this chapter, investigations of the conditioning effects from ergographic exercise of the elbow flexor muscles were described. Under the conditions imposed, both muscular strength and endurance improved significantly. No appreciable deconditioning occurred after a four-week lay-off. In studying the transference of conditioning effects, the mean gain in strength for the nonexercised arm was found to be approximately the same as for the exercised arm; no mean gain in muscular endurance, however, was found for the nonexercised arm.

Chapter 4 / Strength Decrement from Muscle Fatigue

In this chapter, the strength decrement results from muscle fatiguing exercise are presented. In these studies, both the tensiometer and the Kelso-Hellebrandt elbow flexion ergograph were utilized. Muscle fatigue was induced by ergographic exercise; degrees of muscle fatigue were evaluated as the resultant strength decrement, determined as the differences between pre- and post-exercise strengths of the muscles exercised.

According to Marks (72), the first clear-cut recognition of the importance of individual differences in the ergographic fatigue curve was reported by Mosso in 1888 when he noted that the form of the decline in the curve of voluntary muscular work obtained on his ergograph was characteristic of the individual. Mosso observed that "the ergograph thus gives us a record of one of the most intimate and most characteristic features of our individuality—the manner in which we fatigue."

Marks reported several studies showing that individuals have their own characteristics in the way they become fatigued, including a study by Maitz and Sinha. Maitz and Sinha (71) analyzed 119 Mosso ergograph curves and obtained a series of fatigue coefficients. Each curve was divided into groups of ten pulls. In their formula, $FC = \dfrac{X - Y}{X}$, X was the work accomplished in the first ten pulls and Y was the work done in a succeeding set of ten pulls. Thus, the fatigue co-efficient (FC) was the proportionate decrement of work for a given period. They found that individuals differed widely both in the total amount of work done and in the fatigue coefficients for their curves, but that the differences were greater between individuals than between the various curves of a given individual. Other studies utilizing different muscle groups of the same subjects also indicated that the ergographic curve remained fairly constant for the individual.

Strength Decrement and Recovery

In 1953, the writer and associates (10, 39) studied the strength decrement of the elbow flexor muscles following exhaustive exercise on the ergograph. The basic hypothesis explored was that an immediate effect of fatiguing muscles is a reduction of their con-tractile power. Actually, this phenomenon is common enough. For example, at the start, one can do push-ups readily, but as he con-tinues the effort becomes increasingly difficult until the movement is no longer possible.

Considerable information exists which describes the effects of general body endurance activities (running, swimming, and the like) upon heart rate, blood pressure, and other cardiovascular phenomena, as well as the rate of recovery, or return to normal, following such exercise. However, objective evidence was lacking relative to the effects of exhaustive muscular efforts upon strength decrement and strength recovery rate. The study of these effects was the purpose of this research.

The elbow flexor muscles were selected to be studied because of the availability of objective techniques for measuring both their strength and their endurance, as demonstrated in Chapters 2 and 3 of this monograph. It was thus largely possible to isolate the muscles to be studied and to confine the laboratory measurements to the muscles involved.

Procedures

The experimental procedures followed in this study were as follows:

1. The subjects were male college students, most of whom were majoring in physical education. These students were physically superior to college students in general on such tests as the Strength Index, the Physical Fitness Index, and somatotype (predominately mesomorphic).

2. Once each week for six weeks, the subjects exercised their elbow flexor muscles on the Kelso-Hellebrandt ergograph until an exhaustion state was reached; i.e., until the muscles were no longer able to move the ergograph load the slight distance necessary to register on the cumulative distance meter. Insofar as possible, the subjects worked on the ergograph on the same day and hour each week. The left arm was utilized throughout the experiment.

3. Ergography was performed in accordance with the techniques described in Chapter 3. The ergograph load was three-eighths proportion of each subject's elbow flexion strength; the length of the lever arm was eight inches for all subjects; the cadence was one second each for flexion and for extension; all movements were made in a uniformly smooth manner.

4. Cable-tension strength tests of the elbow flexor muscles were given before, 30 seconds after, and at stated intervals for some time following exercise. Graphs were prepared portraying the changes in mean elbow flexion strength.

5. Comparison of the mean elbow flexion strength of the subjects following exercise was made with the pre-exercise mean. The significance of differences between means was tested by application of the *t* ratio. The standard error formula for correlated groups was used, inasmuch as the study was in the nature of a single-group experiment. A one-tail test of significance was applied, based on the assumption

that fatigue would only decrease (not increase) the contractile power of the muscles. The number of subjects for the various exercise sessions varied between 23 and 28. Using 26 as N, a *t*-ratio of 2.49 denotes significance at the .01 level.

Results

Experimentation on strength decrement and strength recovery of the elbow flexor muscles following exhaustive volitional exercise was divided into three phases as follows: (a) using untrained subjects at rest between post-exercise strength tests; (b) using trained subjects under varying conditions between post-exercise strength tests; and (c) using trained subjects, followed for two hours after exercise.

UNTRAINED SUBJECTS AT REST. The first two weeks of the experiment constituted phase one. Prior to this phase, the subjects received instructions in taking ergographic tests and only enough practice to learn the techniques. Since only a minimum of training and muscle conditioning had taken place, the subjects were considered as untrained. Strength tests were administered at the following times after the exhaustive ergographic exercise: 30 seconds, 2½ minutes, 5½ minutes, 8 minutes, 10½ minutes, and every five minutes thereafter, until 45½ minutes had elapsed. The subjects were at rest, lying supine, with minimum movement of the exercised arm between strength tests. The results are portrayed in graph form in Fig. 4.1. The characteristics of these strength decrement curves are:

1. A pronounced drop in strength was found 30 seconds after exercise. The mean decrement was 30 pounds, or 31 per cent, for the first week; and 33 pounds, or 33 per cent, for the second week. The *t* ratios for the differences between the means for the pre-exercise and 30-second strength tests were 12.50 and 10.60 for the first and second weeks respectively. When combined with similar data from another study conducted concurrently, which increased the number of subjects to 51, the *t* ratios were 19.36 and 18.50.

2. An initial rise in mean strength was noted within the next two

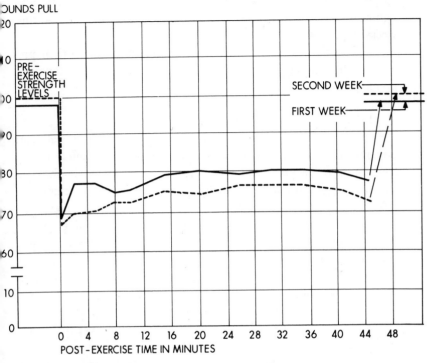

Fig. 4.1 Mean strength decrement curves following exhaustive exercise of elbow flexor muscles—untrained subjects at rest

minutes after exercise. For the first week, this rise was nine pounds, or 30 per cent of the decrement; for the second week, the rise was only three pounds, or 9 per cent of the loss. The differences between the pre-exercise and the 2½-minute strength tests were significant well beyond the .01 level; the t ratios for the first and second weeks were 9.6 and 17.95 respectively.

3. The mean strength recovery curve for the second week, where the initial gain was small, continued to rise until eight minutes had elapsed. Both curves, however, levelled off and showed no appreciable gain throughout the remaining time. The strength decrement means at the end of 40½ minutes after exercise were still 19 per cent and

25 per cent below the pre-exercise levels. These differences are also significant; the *t* ratios were 3.78 and 5.14 for the first and second weeks respectively.

4. Only four subjects, or 14 per cent, had returned to their pre-exercise strength level by the end of 45 minutes after the cessation of exercise.

TRAINED SUBJECTS UNDER VARYING CONDITIONS. For the second phase of the study, different subjects were used. These subjects had not only been instructed in ergographic testing techniques, as was true for those in phase one, but had also participated in four exhaustive exercise sessions on the ergograph prior to their inclusion in this phase of the research. As discovered in other studies previously reported, significant strength and endurance conditioning of the elbow flexor muscles takes place as a result of this amount of ergographic exercise. These subjects, therefore, were considered trained in contrast with those in the first phase, although it is recognized that conditioning could logically continue as the experiment progressed.

Phase two of the study was conducted for three weeks. The conditions of the experiment changed each week. During the first week, subjects moved about the laboratory at will during the time between the strength tests, thus increasing general body circulation. In the second week, subjects did the same as in the first week, but added self-massage (at will) and active movement of the exercised arm; and in the third week, subjects were at rest between strength tests, lying supine, with minimum movements of the exercised arm, as in phase one.

The results of phase two appear graphically in Fig. 4.2. Observations made from these mean strength decrement curves of the elbow flexor muscles are:

1. The curves follow the same general pattern found in the previous phase of the study. The initial drop was pronounced, and was approximately the same as before (29 to 32 per cent). This drop was followed by an initial sharp rise and a levelling off to the end of the time period. The major difference between the two phases is

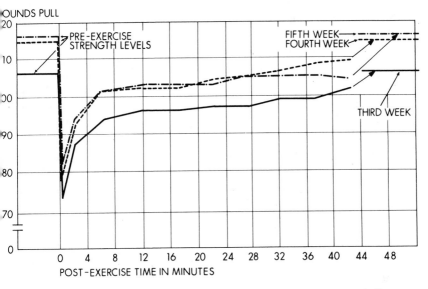

Fig. 4.2 Mean strength decrement curves following exhaustive exercise of elbow flexor muscles—trained subjects under varying conditions

that the trained subjects returned consistently to a higher level at the end of the test period; that is, to 19 and 25 per cent below pre-exercise levels for the untrained subjects and to 5 to 10 per cent for the trained subjects.

2. The usual significance between the strength test means was found for the three weeks of this phase. The *t* ratios were: pre-exercise to 30 seconds after exercise, 12.85 to 17.12; pre-exercise to 2½ minutes after exercise, 6.26 to 10.75; and pre-exercise to 42½ minutes after exercise, 2.84 to 5.76. Although the differences between the pre-exercise and last means were quite small, still they were significant. The final means were preceded by consistently similar test results. Only slight gains in elbow flexor strength were found for all three curves from 12½ minutes after exercise to the end.

3. In this phase, a larger number of subjects reached their pre-exercise elbow flexor strength than was true before. The numbers were: 14 for the third week; 10 for the fourth week; and 6 for the

fifth week. In general, then, more subjects regained their normal strength when permitted to move about and massage their exercised arms than when rest was required between strength tests.

4. The differences in strength recovery for trained subjects when moving about between strength tests and when moving about and massaging the exercised arm were minor in nature and of no consequence. When the subjects were supine and lying at rest between strength tests, however, the mean decrement was greater at the end of the testing time (10 per cent as contrasted with 4 to 5 per cent).

TRAINED SUBJECTS FOLLOWED FOR TWO HOURS. During the third phase of the experiment strength tests were given to the subjects for approximately two hours after exhaustive exercise of the elbow flexor muscles, at the following times: 30 seconds, 2½ minutes, and each 10 minutes thereafter until 122½ minutes had elapsed. The subjects, 18 college men, were permitted to move about and massage their exercised arms at will between strength tests.

Once more, the initial strength decrement mean and the mean strength recovery curve were similar to those previously described. After 12½ minutes, the strength increases were small, with a virtual plateau until 72½ minutes (SDI's from 10 to 7); thereafter, an additional gain of four decrement percentage points occurred, which continued at this level to the end of the testing time (SDI's of 3 or 4). Thus, at the end of two hours, these subjects had not regained their pre-exercise strength mean; in fact, only four subjects had returned to normal at the end of the testing time.

Threshold Fatigue Level

In the University of Oregon Physical Education Research Laboratory, Pastor (77) studied the threshold muscular fatigue level from elbow flexion ergographic exercise and the patterns of strength recovery following various amounts of fatiguing exercise of these muscles. The threshold level was defined as the smallest amount of work to be followed by a significant loss in strength, as measured 30 seconds after ergographic exercise. The interval of 30 seconds after exercise was necessary as this was the minimum time required to change from testing with the ergograph to testing with the tensiometer.

Procedures

The subjects were 210 male university students between 17 and 21 years of age. They were untrained in the various testing techniques involved in the study. The instrument used for exercising the elbow flexor muscles was the Kelso-Hellebrandt ergograph. Single-bout ergographic testing techniques were utilized, in which the weight load was one-fourth proportion of the strength of each subject's elbow flexor muscles and the cadence was 76 beats, or 38 repetitions per minute.

Fourteen situations or degrees of ergographic work of the left elbow flexor muscles formed the basis of the study. Fifteen subjects, assigned by use of a table of random numbers, were tested in each situation. In choosing the various number of repetitions, an attempt was made to provide for the range necessary to determine the threshold level of muscular fatigue at the lower limits and strength decrement and recovery for the entire range of work. The first situation consisted of cable-tension strength tests only, without ergographic exercise. The number of repetitions for the other situations were: 3, 4, 5, 6, 9, 12, 15, 20, 25, 30, 35, 40, and to exhaustion.

Elbow flexion strength tests were administered to all subjects before ergographic exercise and at the following times after the cessation of exercise: 30 seconds, 2½ minutes, 7½ minutes, and 12½ minutes; in exhaustion testing, a strength text was also given 17½ minutes after exercise. The differences between pre-exercise and the several post-exercise strength means were tested for significance by application of the t ratio. For 15 subjects, a t ratio of 1.76 denotes significance at the .05 level. This value of t was chosen (one-tail test) because significance was measured from zero, or no difference, in one direction, since only strength losses occur under conditions of muscular fatigue testing.

Results

THRESHOLD LEVEL. In Table 4.1, the differences between the elbow flexion pre-exercise and the post-exercise means are presented, together with appropriate Strength Decrement Indices (SDI) and the t ratios representing the significance of the differences between means. The Strength Decrement Index is the percentage loss in strength, computed as follows:

$$\text{SDI} = \frac{S_a - S_b}{S_a} \times 100$$

in which S_a = Before-exercise strength
S_b = After-exercise strength

A significant muscular fatigue threshold level 30 seconds after exercise was reached at nine repetitions. The difference between the pre- and post-exercise means was 6.46 pounds; the SDI, 4.99; and the t ratio, 3.00. The mean strength decrements 30 seconds after exercise for 3, 4, 5, and 6 repetitions had t ratios ranging from 1.02 to 1.11; although the amounts of the differences between the means were consistent, they did not reach significance. When the number of ergographic repetitions was more than nine, the increases in mean SDI's were reasonably consistent, reaching 33.34 for exhaustion testing, which was comparable to the studies previously reported in this chapter.

A sudden increase to a t ratio of 7.13 occurred at 15 ergographic repetitions. At 12 repetitions, the t ratio was 3.01; and at 20 repetitions, 3.77. A t ratio as high as 7.13 was not obtained again until the 40-repetitions situation was reached. The mean SDI for 15 repetitions was consistent with the other 30-second, post-exercise results; and the other post-exercise mean SDI's and t ratios, up to 12½ minutes, were generally similar in pattern to the other results. Anticipating, therefore, that the abrupt increase of the t ratio at 15 repetitions (7.13) was due to testing errors, this situation was repeated with an equal

Table 4.1

SIGNIFICANCE OF STRENGTH DECREMENT INDICES OF ELBOW FLEXOR MUSCLES
AFTER VARYING AMOUNTS OF ERGOGRAPHIC WORK
(¼ LOAD AT CADENCE OF 76 BEATS PER MINUTE)

POST-EXERCISE

REPETITIONS	30 Seconds			2½ Minutes			7½ Minutes			12½ Minutes			17½ Minutes		
	Diff.	SDI	t	Diff.	SDI	t	Diff.	SDI	t	Diff.	SDI	t	Diff.	SDI	t
0	0.06	-0.06	0.03	4.34	3.14	1.48	4.60	3.33	1.43	11.20	8.12	3.58			
3	4.20	3.22	1.06	7.40	5.67	2.02	10.40	7.96	2.87	8.47	6.49	1.83			
4	4.66	3.43	1.07	8.33	6.13	2.32	9.06	6.67	2.63	2.73	2.01	0.75			
5	3.07	2.52	1.02	5.87	4.82	1.81	5.87	4.82	1.59	5.14	4.22	1.33			
6	4.53	3.31	1.11	5.20	3.80	1.20	9.47	6.91	2.12	7.13	5.20	1.23			
9	6.46	4.99	3.00	3.26	2.52	0.82	3.46	2.67	0.68	3.33	2.57	0.87			
12	10.60	7.81	3.01	7.07	5.21	2.24	9.47	6.98	3.44	8.67	6.39	3.00			
15	16.46	12.91	7.13	6.06	4.75	2.05	8.46	6.63	2.97	9.66	7.57	2.95			
20	20.06	15.42	3.77	13.60	10.45	2.66	15.13	11.63	3.95	16.13	12.40	3.55			
25	18.54	14.17	4.80	19.40	14.82	4.67	15.60	11.92	3.93	20.80	15.89	4.36			
30	37.74	27.70	6.25	23.94	17.57	7.21	21.87	16.05	8.01	23.74	17.42	6.84			
35	32.20	25.89	5.76	20.40	16.46	4.58	16.00	12.91	3.16	20.20	16.30	6.43			
40	30.67	25.67	10.05	18.20	15.23	8.54	18.20	15.23	8.24	18.07	15.13	8.40			
Exhaust.	45.67	33.34	11.45	21.47	15.62	6.41	16.33	11.92	6.38	16.60	12.11	4.87	16.20	11.82	5.68

number of new subjects. However, comparable results were obtained; the mean SDI was 11.53 as compared with the original mean of 12.91 and the *t* ratio was 6.95 as compared with 7.13. No valid explanation can be advanced for this occurrence.

While the situations with repetitions below nine did not produce significant mean elbow flexion strength decrements 30 seconds after exercise, such decrements did occur later during the post-exercise periods. At 2½ minutes after exercise, they were significant at the .05 level for three, four, and five repetitions; however, this significance was not maintained at the later test times. The taking of two maximum strength tests within 2½ minutes after exercise could well have induced additional fatigue.

An inconsistent finding was found in the situation without ergographic exercise. A significant mean elbow flexion strength loss of 11.20 pounds was obtained at 12½ minutes after exercise; the SDI was 8.12 and the *t* ratio was 3.58. To check the accuracy of this situation, new subjects were tested under the same conditions; comparable results were obtained. Thus, the repetition of maximal strength tests as spaced in this study produced a significant strength decrement.

STRENGTH RECOVERY. The strength recovery pattern following exhaustive ergographic exercise of the left elbow flexor muscles was similar to that described earlier and portrayed in Fig. 4.2 for the third week. However, the ergographic testing conditions were not identical: In the earlier study, the ergograph load was three-eighths proportion of elbow flexion strength and the cadence was 60; the subjects had had four ergographic sessions of practice and training; and they remained supine resting between post-exercise strength tests. In this study, the ergograph load was one-fourth proportion of elbow flexion strength and the cadence was 76; the subjects did not have prior ergographic experience; and they moved about between post-exercise strength tests.

The strength recovery curves for 30, 35, and 40 repetitions were comparable to each other and to the pattern obtained for exhaustive exercise. The recovery curves following mild exercise showed some inconsistencies. However, the mean strength scores after exercise did not reach the pre-exercise strength means; quite logically, some muscular fatigue could have been continued as a result of the periodic post-exercise strength testing.

Motivation

Again in the University of Oregon Physical Education Research Laboratory, Nelson (75) studied the effects of applying various motivational situations to college men who were subjected to a stressful physical performance involving exercise to the point of exhaustion on the elbow flexion ergograph. The effects evaluated were the amount of work done on the ergograph, the strength decrement, and the rate of strength recovery following the exhaustive exercise.

Motivational Situations

Ten motivational situations were devised for use in this study, as follows:

1. *Normal Instructions:* The subjects were merely instructed to exercise as long as they could.

2. *Verbal Encouragement:* While the subjects were exercising, the investigator verbally encouraged them to continue exercising as long as possible.

3. *Individual Competition:* Two subjects were brought to the testing room and asked to compete against each other to obtain the highest cumulative distance score on the ergograph.

4. *Group Competition:* The subjects were shown a scale chart of the purported ergographic performances of college men; they were encouraged to determine their physical fitness status in relation to their classmates.

5. *Obtainable Goal:* Each subject was directed to exercise for 40 repetitions; this goal was high, but obtainable.

6. *Observer's Presence:* After the exercise began, an official-look-

ing observer walked in and watched the proceedings with apparent interest.

7. *Instructor Interest:* Before each subject reported for ergographic testing, his physical education service course teacher urged him to do his best and asked him to report his score when he returned to class.

8. *Ego-involvement:* In a casual manner, before exercise was started, each subject was told that junior high school pupils had averaged 62 repetitions and that senior high school students had averaged more than 70 repetitions on the ergograph. The investigator remarked that he was sure the subject would do better than these boys did. These norms were fictitious and extremely high; actually, they were considered unattainable. (Besides ego-involvement, a goal is included in this motivational situation.)

9. *Air Force Space Program:* The subjects were told that they were taking part in the Air Force space program and that standards were being set for a number of different tasks in future selection of astronauts.

10. *Competition with Russian Students:* The subjects were told that the University was cooperating in a nation-wide study designed to compare the performances of American college students in a variety of tests of strength and endurance with recently released results of Russian students' performances on the same tests.

Procedures

The subjects participating in this study were 250 male students from physical education service classes at the University of Oregon who were between 18 and 24 years of age. These subjects were randomly selected from all students in physical education service courses by use of a table of random numbers. Students who were known by the investigator were excluded in order to eliminate any potential motivation influence resulting from such previous association.

Twenty-five subjects were tested in each of the ten motivational situations. For all motivational situations but individual competition, only one subject was in the testing room at a time; observers of the testing were not admitted. Every effort was made to keep the motivational situations as realistic as possible; these procedures are described in detail by Nelson in his dissertation.

The Kelso-Hellebrandt ergograph was used for exercising the left elbow flexor muscles. Single-bout ergographic testing techniques carried to exhaustion were utilized. The weight load was one-fourth proportion of the strength of the subject's elbow flexor muscles and the cadence was 76, or 38 repetitions per minute. Inasmuch as the ergograph weight loads were adapted to each individual as a proportion of the strength of the muscles exercised, the cumulative distance the weight load was moved was used as the measure of ergographic performance.

Elbow flexion strength tests were administered to each subject before ergographic exercise and before he was exposed to a particular motivational situation. This test was repeated 30 seconds, 2½ minutes, and 7½ minutes after cessation of the exercise. The differences between means were tested for significance by application of the *t* ratio.

Cumulative Distance Results

In summarizing the results of Nelson's study, three classifications of motivational groups may be formed, based upon the mean cumulative distance the ergograph loads were raised; these groups, however, were not mutually exclusive, as will be seen. The three classifications are known as low, moderate, and high groups. The differences between these cumulative distance means appear in Table 4.2.

Low groups. This classification consisted of the three motivational situations producing the lowest cumulative distance means; these were for normal instructions, verbal encouragement, and instructor interest (1, 2, and 7).

1. The mean cumulative distances for these groups ranged from

Table 4.2

DIFFERENCES BETWEEN MEANS OF CUMULATIVE DISTANCE SCORES FOR ELBOW FLEXION ERGOGRAPHIC PERFORMANCES
(in centimeters)

| | | | | | Situations | | | | | | | |
1	2	3	4	5	6	7	8	9	10	Diff.	D_m	t
1157.0	1190.0									33.0	44.8	0.74
1157.0		1321.9								164.9	39.4	4.19†
1157.0			1284.5							127.5	57.2	2.23*
1157.0				1289.9						132.9	26.6	4.99†
1157.0					1241.4					84.4	36.2	2.33*
1157.0						1185.3				28.3	42.1	0.67
1157.0							1419.8			262.8	58.9	4.46†
1157.0								1361.0		204.0	49.5	4.12†
1157.0									1311.9	154.9	41.8	3.71†
	1190.0	1321.9								131.9	47.4	2.97†
	1190.0		1284.5							94.5	61.9	1.53
	1190.0			1289.9						99.9	37.4	2.68†
	1190.0				1241.4					51.4	44.7	1.15
	1190.0					1185.3				4.7	49.7	0.09
	1190.0						1419.8			229.8	64.5	3.56†
	1190.0							1361.0		171.0	56.0	3.05†
	1190.0								1311.9	121.9	49.4	2.46*
		1321.9	1284.5							37.4	55.4	0.67
		1321.9		1289.9						32.0	30.7	1.04
		1321.9			1241.4					80.5	39.2	2.05*
		1321.9				1185.3				136.6	44.8	3.05†
		1321.9					1419.8			97.9	64.6	1.51
		1321.9						1361.0		39.1	51.8	0.76
		1321.9							1311.9	10.0	44.5	0.22
			1284.5	1289.9						5.4	47.2	0.11
			1284.5		1241.4							

						Situations						
1	2	3	4	5	6	7	8	9	10	Diff.	D_m	t
			1284.5				1419.8			135.3	70.7	1.91
			1284.5					1361.0		76.5	67.8	1.13
			1284.5						1311.9	27.4	58.1	0.47
				1289.9	1241.4					48.5	26.4	1.83
				1289.9		1185.3				104.6	34.1	3.06†
				1289.9			1419.8			129.9	53.5	2.43*
				1289.9				1361.0		71.1	42.9	1.66
				1289.9					1311.9	22.0	33.7	0.66
					1241.4	1185.3				56.1	42.0	1.34
					1241.4		1419.8			178.4	60.2	2.96†
					1241.4			1361.0		119.6	49.4	2.42*
					1241.4				1311.9	70.5	41.7	1.70
						1185.3	1419.8			234.5	67.5	3.47†
						1185.3		1361.0		175.7	53.9	3.26†
						1185.3			1311.9	126.6	46.9	2.69†
							1419.8	1361.0		58.8	67.9	0.87
							1419.8		1311.9	107.9	62.5	1.73
								1361.0	1311.9	49.1	53.6	0.91

* Difference between means reaches significance at the .05 level.
† Difference between means reaches significance at the .01 level.

KEY

Situation
1. Normal Instructions
2. Verbal Encouragement
3. Individual Competition
4. Group Competition
5. Obtainable Goal
6. Observer's Presence
7. Instructor Interest
8. Ego-involvement
9. Air Force Space Program
10. Competition with Russians

1157.0 to 1190.0 cm. Thus, the differences between the means were slight, not exceeding 33.0 cm., and they were not significant.

2. All three of the means were significantly lower than the means of five other groups, individual competition, obtainable goal, ego-involvement, Air Force space program, and competition with Russians. In addition, the normal instructions group had a lower mean than the means of the group competition and observer's presence groups.

3. Two of the low groups, normal instructions and instructor interest, had comparable variability as well; their respective standard deviations were 129.7 and 135.9 cm. respectively. The standard deviation for the verbal encouragement group was higher, 185.6 cm.

HIGH GROUPS. Three motivational situations produced the highest cumulative distance means; these were ego-involvement, Air Force space program, and individual competition (8, 9, and 3).

1. The cumulative distance means for these three groups were: 1419.8 cm., ego-involvement; 1361.0 cm., Air Force space program; and 1321.9 cm., individual competition. The differences between these means were not significant.

2. All three of these means were significantly higher than the means of the following four groups: normal instructions, verbal encouragement, instructor interest, and observer's presence. In addition, the ego-involvement mean was significantly higher than the obtainable goal mean.

3. The ego-involvement group had the highest standard deviation obtained (268.1 cm.) in the study. The Air Force space program group was also high, 213.7 cm. The individual competition group had a moderate standard deviation of 150.7 cm.

MODERATE GROUPS. The moderate classification was composed of four motivational situations, as follows: obtainable goal, observer's presence, group competition, and competition with Russians (5, 6, 4, and 10).

1. The mean cumulative distances the ergograph loads were

raised were comparable for three of the moderate groups. The means for the obtainable goal, group competition, and competition with Russian groups ranged from 1284.5 to 1311.9 cm., the difference being 27.4 cm. The mean for the observer's presence group was lower, 1241.4 cm. However, the differences between the means of these four groups were not significant.

2. Placement of these four groups in the moderate category was not clear-cut. In relation to the low groups, the means of the obtainable goal and competition with Russians groups were significantly higher than the three low group means; however, the observer's presence and the group competition means were significantly higher than the mean of the normal instructions group only. In relation to the high groups, the group competition and competition with Russians means were not significantly lower than any of the high group means; the mean of the observer's presence group was significantly lower than all three of the high group means; the obtainable goal mean was significantly lower than the mean of only the ego-involvement group.

3. The smallest standard deviation of all ten motivational situations was found for the obtainable goal group, 35.4 cm. This classification also contained one of the highest standard deviations, 235.5 cm. for the group competition group. The remaining two groups with moderate cumulative distance means had standard deviations of 128.7 and 166.6 cm. for observer's presence and competition with Russian groups respectively.

Strength Decrement Results

Table 4.3 contains the mean strength indices and the rate of strength recovery following exhaustive ergographic exercise conducted in the ten motivational situations. The table is arranged according to the low, high, and moderate classifications described above. The results of Pastor's study, previously presented in this chapter, are also included for purposes of comparison; inasmuch as Pastor used verbal encouragement in ergographic testing, his results appear with the low groups. Observations pertaining to these results follow:

Table 4.3

MEAN STRENGTH DECREMENT INDICES AND RATE OF STRENGTH
RECOVERY OF SUBJECTS IN TEN MOTIVATIONAL SITUATIONS

	Mean Distance Load Moved	SDI 30 sec.	Gain	SDI 2½ min.	Gain	SDI 7½ min.
Low Groups						
Situation 1, Normal Instructions	1157.0	34.8	17.4	17.4	4.7	12.7
Situation 7, Instructor Interest	1185.3	35.9	17.2	18.7	5.6	13.1
Situation 2, Verbal Encouragement	1190.0	37.7	19.0	18.7	5.5	13.2
Pastor's Study	1014.0	33.3	17.7	15.6	3.7	11.9
High Groups						
Situation 8, Ego-involvement	1419.8	51.5	11.9	39.6	8.7	30.9
Situation 9, Air Force Space Program	1361.0	45.2	9.7	35.5	8.7	26.8
Situation 3, Individual Competition	1321.9	42.4	9.1	33.3	7.2	26.1
Moderate Groups						
Situation 5, Obtainable Goal	1289.9	46.7	9.8	36.9	9.7	27.2
Situation 6, Observer's Presence	1241.4	44.9	11.7	33.2	8.4	24.8
Situation 4, Group Competition	1284.5	43.1	11.2	31.9	8.0	23.9
Situation 10, Competition with Russians	1311.9	42.7	12.8	29.9	7.9	22.0

1. The mean strength decrement indices (SDI) 30 seconds after exercise for the three groups in the low classification and in Pastor's study were the smallest obtained in this investigation; they were similar, ranging narrowly from 33.3 to 37.7. The mean gains in recovery 2½ minutes after exercise were also comparable, the SDI's being between 15.6 and 18.7. The same was true at 7½ minutes after exercise; the indices were between 11.9 and 13.2.

2. The mean SDI's for the three motivational situations with highest cumulative distance means were also highest. The ego-

involvement group had the highest SDI's obtained in the study; these were 51.5 at 30 seconds, 39.6 at 2½ minutes, and 30.9 at 7½ minutes. The strength decrement 7½ minutes after exercise for this group was approximately the same as the decrements of the low groups 30 seconds after exercise.

3. The strength decrement and strength recovery patterns for the moderate motivational groups were similar to those for the high groups.

Summary

In this chapter, the muscular fatigue effects from volitional exhaustive exercise of the elbow flexor muscles on the Kelso-Hellebrandt ergograph were investigated. The basic hypothesis explored was that the immediate effect of fatiguing muscles is to reduce their contractile power; this hypothesis was definitely supported. Under the conditions imposed, a characteristic mean strength decrement recovery curve was obtained.

Other factors investigated in relation to muscular fatigue were: the strength decrement and strength recovery following fatiguing exercise for trained and untrained subjects; the differences in strength recovery rate when subjects were resting and were moving about during the recovery period; the threshold level of muscular fatigue under a specified work situation; and the comparative effects of various motivational situations on work done on the ergograph and the rate of recovery following such work.

Chapter *5* / **Strength Decrement Index Applications**

The studies reported in Chapter 4 supported the hypothesis that the immediate effect of fatiguing muscles is to reduce their ability to apply tension. It was also demonstrated that this effect can be measured as the amount of strength decrement resulting from fatiguing activity. The Strength Decrement Index was established as a means of measuring muscular fatigue. In this chapter, investigations in which this index was used to evaluate the muscular fatigue effects of participation in strenuous physical activity will be described.

Initial Pack-Carrying Study

The first strength decrement application study to be presented deals with three problems: the identification of the muscle groups subjected to fatigue from pack carrying; the determination of the degree of such fatigue related to varrying amounts of the load; and the influence of pack position on the body upon the pattern of muscular fatigue (40). The results of this applied research should be of interest to hikers and campers and to those phases of the military services where packs are carried. Further, identifying the muscles under greatest stress in a specific pack-carrying situation will enable effective direction of efforts to condition these muscles for this function. This study and the pack-carrying studies which follow were conducted by the writer at Springfield College under subsidy from the Quartermaster Corps, Department of the Army.

Throughout history, armies have been faced with the problem of supplying soldiers with clothing and personal equipment, food and shelter, weapons and ammunition. The problem is relatively simple when soldiers are in encampment; on the move and in combat, it is much more difficult. The expanding scale of military operations and changes in technology have increased greatly the complexity of this situation.

In the solution of supply problems, the infantryman has necessarily been forced to transport essential and immediately needed items of equipment on his person. The foot soldier of early armies, such as the Roman legionnaire, as well as the infantry man of France, Russia, Germany, and Japan prior to 1900, carried a load of 60 to 65 pounds and more. Frequently these soldiers reached the battlefield in such a fatigued state that effective combat was impossible (8). As has been true in modern wars, much of the equipment thus carried was thrown away along the route of march. The soldier in combat frequently discarded everything he could do without with no particular concern as to what happened to it.

Much has been written and said on the problem of what, where, and how much the soldier should carry. Despite all the controversy over the centuries, little scientific evidence is available for the solution of this problem, decisions, for the most part, being based upon opinion. The lack of factual data has been the single greatest deterrent to the development of a completely functional system of load carrying. The Quartermaster Corps, United States Army, has conducted investigations into the design of special packs and into ways of lightening the weight of essential items of equipment. Through its Climatic Research Laboratory, the effects of pack carrying on the human organism are being investigated under experimental conditions.

A review of the physiological research studies on pack carrying has been presented by Bailey and McDermott (3). In the main, these studies have two characteristics: (a) The evaluative processes have been based largely on metabolic determiners, and to a lesser extent on electromyographic techniques, center-of-gravity measurements, and the judgment of subjects. (b) The experimental procedures have been confined mostly to treadmill marching, thus without reference to the field conditions encountered by soldiers or by hikers over uneven terrain. The reviewers conclude that the results so far obtained are meager and frequently inconclusive.

Shortcomings of the investigations reported are as follows: (a) Many studies were based upon limited observations of a small number of subjects. (b) The state of training and other descriptive measures of the subjects were not known. (c) Psychological motivational factors in pack-carrying performance were ignored. (d) Energy cost studies do not adequately reflect the fatigue of local muscle groups. (e) Only muscles directly underlying the pick-up electrodes can be investigated by electromyography; and there is no differentiation between action and stabilizing muscles. (f) There was no reliable measure used for determining degrees of muscular contraction. (g) The center-of-gravity studies were conducted largely from a standing rather than a marching position.

Field Conditions

FIELD COURSE. This and the other pack-carrying studies to follow were conducted under field conditions. The field course was 1.25 miles long over moderately rough and hilly terrain. Each march was 7.5 miles long, requiring six repetitions of the course.

The site was surveyed to divide it into squares of 200 feet. From these survey lines, the course was laid out, starting and ending at a testing station. The survey lines were superimposed on a topographical map of the area, as shown in Fig. 5.1. The heavy broken line indicates the trail used for the field course. The trail had one steep incline covering approximately 150 feet of trail distance; the remaining portion consisted of gradual ascents and descents interspersed with about the same amount of level ground.

RATE OF MARCH. A major problem in establishing the experimental field situation was to devise a method for regulating the rate of march, in order to keep the speed at which the course was traversed as constant as could ordinarily be expected in field conditions. It was, of course, essential that all subjects maintain approximately the same pace for all phases of the investigation.

The basic unit of time and distance selected was patterned after the military concept of 50 minutes of marching followed by ten minutes of rest. The distance adopted was in units of 2.5 miles, twice around the course in 50 minutes or 88 yards in one minute. This rate conforms well with research reported by Brezina and Reichel (5) and by Cathcart, Richardson, and Campbell (9) to the effect that maximum efficiency of energy cost in marching was between 80 and 95 yards per minute. The former authors also indicated that energy cost was not significantly affected by loads up to 46 pounds. Heavier loads require an excessive increase in energy cost; however, it is more economical to increase the load than to increase the rate of march.

A number of pace-control systems were considered. The following method was adopted as being realistic in terms of Army field marching conditions.

1. A relay timing device was designed and constructed to discharge electrically every five minutes; the discharge was for three seconds.

2. Four claxons, pointing in different directions at right angles to each other, were mounted atop the structure housing the testing station. These were wired to the timing device. They could be heard clearly at all points on the trail.

3. Markers were placed on the trail at points the subjects should reach during each successive period of five minutes; these points are shown on the map (Fig. 5.1). The locations of the markers were

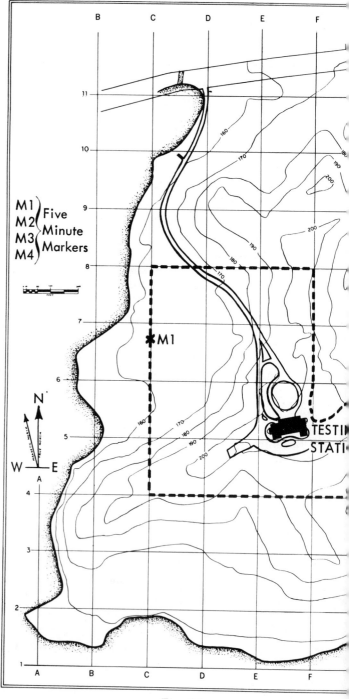

Fig. 5.1

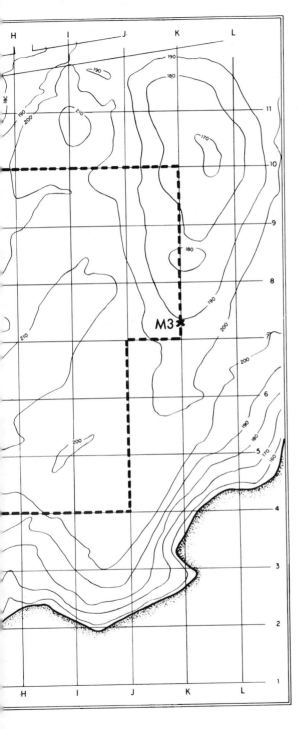

determined by walking the course repeatedly, marking on each trip the spot reached when the horns blew. The final positions of the markers were selected as those best representing completion of the trail in 50 minutes. In the pack-carrying experiments, these markers served as check points: if a subject was short of the proper marker when the claxons sounded, he increased the pace a bit; if he had passed the marker, he slowed appropriately.

This method of regulating the rate of march proved entirely satisfactory. The subjects were able to pace themselves to reach the markers within 15 seconds before or after the sounding of the claxons.

EQUIPMENT. The subjects were provided with regulation army clothing, combat boots, equipment, packs, and M-1 rifles. Thus, they were dressed and the load distributed on the person in accordance with Army regulations, with the exception of the packs, which were varied for purposes of the study. The items carried other than the rifle and pack were cartridge belt (lead weights to simulate ammunition), dummy grenades, bayonet knife, entrenching tool, and canteen.

Strength Decrement Testing

Strength decrement was the basic measure used to evaluate the muscle fatigue effects from carrying packs on military marches. For each muscle group on each march, the pre-exercise strength mean was compared with the means at the end of each 2.5 miles of marching.

The muscle groups tested were those considered to be: (a) under direct stress in supporting the packs, (b) involved in stabilizing the body in relation to the pack, (c) primarily activated in marching, and (d) affected by interference with circulation caused by pressure from pack straps. The following 11 muscle groups were thus selected, listed in the order tested: right grip, left grip, ankle plantar flexors, shoulder horizontal flexors, knee extensors, knee flexors, hip flexors, hip extensors, trunk flexors, trunk extensors, and shoulder elevators. For the shoulder (except shoulder elevators), hip, knee, and ankle strength measures, the left side only was tested. The order of test administration was adopted to facilitate rapid testing of the subjects, as all 11 tests were given during the 10-minute "rest" period following each 50 minutes of marching.

The grip strength tests were given with a manuometer (14). All other strength tests, except for the shoulder elevators and the ankle plantar flexors, were administered by cable-tension methods as recorded with a tensiometer (28). The ankle plantar flexion test was also given as described for cable-tension procedures, except that a combat boot was worn and shoulder blocks were used; to record the great amount of strength thus exerted, a chain and dynamometer, rather than a cable and tensiometer, were utilized.

For the shoulder elevation strength test, a harness going over both shoulders was devised. The subject stood erect with knees, hips, and back straight; the harness was attached to a dynamometer anchored between his feet. The shoulder elevation (or shoulder shrug) movement is especially powerful: the highest score obtained was 880 lbs.; the median was 520 lbs.

It should be observed, obviously, that all strength tests could not be given at the same instant each 2.5 miles of marching was completed. Some tests were given immediately, while others were delayed as much as eight or nine minutes. According to evidence presented in the preceding chapter, the most pronounced strength recovery from fatiguing exercise occurs during the first few minutes and continues at a decelerated rate for 12 minutes. Consequently, considerable strength recovery should have occurred in the muscles tested last in the sequence.

Marches

Subjects. The subjects were 30 Springfield College students majoring in physical education. The age range was from 18 to 26 years. The following median scores will further describe this group: height, 69.9 in.; weight, 167 lbs.; Physical Fitness Index, 104; and Strength Index, 3013.

Before the pack-carrying experiment commenced, the subjects

were taken to the marching area in small groups and were oriented to the purpose of the study. Then they were taken over the field course with packs, so as to become familiar with the trail and the rate of march which would be necessary. The strength testing sequence was explained and they went through the process of test administration.

EXPLORATORY MARCH. A preliminary march was conducted to observe the distances the subjects unconditioned for marching could go, and the point in load carrying where strength decrements occurred for the various muscle groups studied. Inasmuch as the rifles and grenades had not arrived at this time, the subjects marched without this weight. A combat pack was carried located high on the back in the customary manner. The over-all load weighed 29 pounds.

The subjects were asked to march as far as they could under the prescribed conditions. The majority of the subjects discontinued the march at 7.5 miles; the elapsed time was three hours. Many of the muscle groups showed strength losses due to the strain of marching and carrying the load from 2.5 miles and beyond. As a consequence, 7.5 miles was adopted as the marching distance for the balance of the study.

MARCH VARIATIONS. Six experimental marches were conducted, one each week. The amount of weight carried, the type of pack, and the location of the pack on the body were varied. Only one such factor was changed at a time, however, so that the effects of the variation would be uninvolved with other changes. The conditions of the six marches were as follows:

March No. 1: Combat pack without rifle; weight* 29 lbs.; pack carried high on back; winter clothing.

March No. 2: Same as March No. 1, except with rifle; weight, 41 lbs.

---

* The weights given include all equipment carried by the subjects, not the weight of the pack alone.

March No. 3: Same as March No. 2, except with pack carried low on back.

March No. 4: No pack, load, or equipment; summer fatigues.

March No. 5: Rucksack with rifles and grenades; weight, 41 lbs.; summer fatigues.

March No. 6: Same as March No. 5, except with 61 lbs. (which equals the field-load weight of the rifleman, but not the pack carried).

Results

A summary of the results of the pack-carrying study appears in Table 5.1. Both mean SDI's and *t* ratios above 1.50 (representing the significance between pre- and post-march means) are given for each muscle group on each march. Significant *t* ratios, when probability is limited to one tail, is 1.70 at the .05 level. The standard error formula for correlated groups was used in these computations, inasmuch as this study was in the nature of a one-group experiment.

Eight muscle groups, all except the right and left grips and shoulder horizontal flexors, had *t* ratios above 1.50 for at least three of the marches. The exceptions noted did not produce significant results for any of the pack carries, so were eliminated from Table 5.1 and from further consideration in this report. The grip strength tests were included in this research because it was thought that the pressure from the pack straps in carrying military loads might reduce their strength, as a consequence of interference with blood circulation to the arms and hands. However, such results were not obtained from these tests.

Observations of the strength losses resulting from the various marches are as follows:

1. Carrying a 41-lb. load with the rucksack resulted in the least over-all strength loss of the muscle groups tested. Only three muscle groups, all located in the lower body (marching muscles), had strength losses which were significant near and beyond the .05 level; these groups were the hip flexors, hip extensors, and ankle plantar flexors.

2. With the rucksack, also, the effect on total strength loss with

Table 5.1

SUMMARIZATION OF STRENGTH DECREMENT INDICES
FOR THE SIX EXPERIMENTAL MARCHES

March	Mean	Muscle Groups							
		Shoulder Elevators	Trunk Flexors	Trunk Extensors	Hip Flexors	Hip Extensors	Knee Flexors	Knee Extensors	Ankle Plantar Flexors
1. 29-lb. high combat pack	SDI		9.31	11.19	3.64	6.34	13.78	5.19	3.57
	t		1.72	2.00	2.29	1.74	4.20	1.53	1.65
2. 41-lb. high combat pack	SDI		3.18	3.70	4.21	5.04	13.01	5.48	3.64
	t		1.71	2.50	2.50	2.30	4.59	3.54	2.18
3. 41-lb. low combat pack	SDI	10.28	4.30	8.09	5.97	4.28	10.30	4.99	4.49
	t	5.30	1.57	1.75	2.16	2.43	3.13	2.00	2.19
4. No load	SDI		7.84	6.40					4.68
	t		2.00	1.71					2.13
5. 41-lb. rucksack	SDI				4.36	3.46			3.29
	t				1.60	1.62			2.14
6. 61-lb. rucksack	SDI	10.10	8.08	14.64	5.35	5.75	6.46		6.58
	t	2.79	4.67	4.53	2.40	1.67	2.47		2.86

the 61-lb. load was approximately the same as for the combat pack with 41 lbs. carried low on the back. However, the proportionate amount of loss for the different muscle groups varied: with the ruck-sack, greater loss was found for the trunk flexors and extensors; with the combat pack, the larger decrements were for the shoulder eleva-tors and the knee extensors.

3. Very little difference in over-all strength loss was found be-tween the 41-lb. high and low combat pack marches, although there were differences in the muscles affected. The greater losses were: knee flexors and extensors for the high pack; and shoulder elevators for the low pack.

4. With no load, three muscle groups were involved, the trunk flexors and extensors and the ankle plantar flexors. From observing the results of the other marches, it was judged that loads up to 41 lbs. did not affect the mean SDI's of these muscle groups beyond those involved in marching the 7.5 miles. However, when the load was increased beyond this weight, definite additional stress was found, as shown for the 61-lb. rucksack march.

5. The knee flexor muscles had the greatest total strength loss on the six experimental marches. However, the strain on these muscles was centered primarily in the first three and the last marches, with t ratios of 4.20, 4.59, 3.13, and 2.47 respectively. As was sub-sequently found, the amount of knee flexion strength loss for the final march, when the subjects were in their best marching condi-tion, was the most significant single SDI in correlating with motor-physical fitness tests. The correlations were: $-.54$, with Strength Index; $-.49$, with AAF Physical Fitness Test; $-.45$, with Navy Standard Physical Fitness Index. In interpreting these correlations, r's of .35 and .45 are significant at the .05 and .01 levels respectively.

6. For the shoulder elevator muscles, only two marches produced significant mean SDI's, the 41-lb. low combat pack and the 61-lb. rucksack. In both of these marches, the load was carried low but with straps over the shoulders, thus resulting in a long pull on the shoulder muscles. The effect of this pull was not noted with the rucksack (41 lbs.) until the weight became much greater (61 lbs.), which may

be accounted for by the brace construction of this pack providing support at the hips.

7. The knee extensors had the least mean strength losses of the eight muscle groups. They followed much the same pattern, but in lesser degree, as did the knee flexors, except no significant mean strength loss was found for the 61-lb. rucksack march. This exception may be due to the better condition of the subjects on the final march in the series.

8. Mean strength losses of over 10 per cent were found in seven muscle groups during the marches. The SDI's were as follows: 14.64, trunk extensors with 61-lb. rucksack; 13.78 and 13.01, knee flexors with 29-lb. and 41-lb. high combat packs respectively; 11.19, trunk extensors, with 29-lb. high combat pack; and 10.28 and 10.10 shoulder elevators, with 41-lb. low combat pack and 61-lb. rucksack respectively.

PER CENT SDI

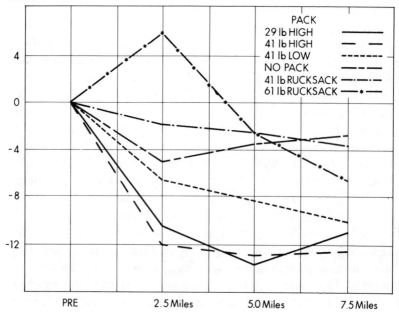

Fig. 5.2   Knee flexion mean SDI's pack-carrying

Tables, graphs, and discussions of the mean SDI's for each muscle group at 2.5, 5.0, and 7.5 miles for the various marches are too detailed to include in this presentation. To show the nature of these data, however, the mean strength decrements of the knee flexor muscles are presented in Fig. 5.2.

Nearly the full strength decrement effect on the knee flexor muscles was felt in the first 2.5 miles of the first two marches, the 29-lb. and 41-lb. high combat packs; they continued at about the same level for the balance of the marches. With the 41-lb. low combat pack, the decrement line rose sharply at 2.5 miles (about two-thirds of the total loss), after which it continued as a straight-line rise but at a lessened rate. The 61-lb. rucksack march produced an increase in strength at 2.5 miles, followed by a rapid decline to 7.5 miles; however, the final SDI of 6.46 is not significant at the .05 level. The decrements for the other two marches, no pack and 41-lb. rucksack, were slight and not significant.

Second Pack-Carrying Study

Conditioning Effects

In the preceding pack-carrying study, no effort was made to control the physical conditioning effect on the subjects from repeated 7.5-mile marches. That such conditioning took place is readily concluded from the evidence presented below.

INCREASE IN STRENGTH OF THE MUSCLE GROUPS TESTED. The mean pre-march strength scores for each muscle group tested were computed before the first and last experimental marches. Thus, five 7.5-mile marches intervened between tests. The results appear in Table 5.2.

The increase in strength of the involved muscles was definite. The differences between the means for three muscle groups were significant beyond the .01 level: trunk extensors (39.9 lbs.), trunk flexors (36.3 lbs.), and shoulder elevators (71.7 lbs.). The gain in

Table 5.2

INCREASE IN STRENGTH OF INVOLVED MUSCLES AS A RESULT OF FIVE 7.5-MILE MILITARY MARCHES

| | Means before | | | | |
| | First | Last | | S. E. | |
Muscle Group	March	March	Diff.	Diff.	t Ratio
Trunk extensors	124.6	164.5	39.9	8.55	4.67
Trunk flexors	121.6	157.9	36.3	8.82	4.12
Shoulder elevators	452.3	524.0	71.7	22.47	3.19
Hip flexors	155.5	170.1	14.6	5.99	2.44
Ankle plantar flexors	370.8	388.9	18.1	11.98	1.51
Hip extensors	111.4	113.2	1.8	6.26	0.29
Knee flexors	118.2	119.5	1.3		
Knee extensors	217.0	217.8	0.8		

mean strength for the hip flexors (14.6 lbs.) was nearly significant at the .01 level; and the mean gain for the ankle plantar flexors (18.1 lbs.) was noticeable, but did not reach the .05 level of significance.

Furthermore, the over-all percentage in mean loss of strength was less and generally occurred late on the march (7.5 miles) than on the first part of the march (2.5 to 5.0 miles). This observation, however, should be interpreted cautiously, as the conditions were not identical, the packs being different for the two marches. However, the load was 20 lbs. heavier for the final march, which would logically have caused greater strength losses.

Increase in Motor-Physical Fitness Test Scores

Before the exploratory march and after the last experimental march (seven marches thus intervening), several motor-physical fitness test batteries were administered to the subjects. The mean scores for this testing appear in Table 5.3.

The means for all motor fitness tests increased during the pack-carrying study. All increases but one were significant beyond the .05 level. The exception is McCloy's Arm-Strength Score with a *t* ratio of 1.64, which nearly reaches the .05 level of significance. All three

Table 5.3

COMPARISON OF MEANS ON MOTOR-PHYSICAL FITNESS TESTS
BEFORE AND AFTER SEVEN MILITARY
PACK-CARRYING MARCHES

Motor-Physical Fitness Test	Initial Mean	Final Mean	Diff.	S. E. Diff.	t Ratio
1. Army Physical Efficiency Test	253	281	28	4.6	6.1
2. AAF Physical Fitness Test	56	59	3	0.6	5.0
3. Navy Standard Physical Fitness Test	260	275	15	3.0	5.0
4. Physical Fitness Index	104	113	9	2.0	4.5
5. Strength Index	3084	3407	323	142.0	2.3
6. McCloy Arm Strength Score	581	591	10	6.1	1.6

of the armed forces motor fitness tests showed definite gains, especially the Army Physical Efficiency Test, which had a *t* ratio of 6.1. The final mean of 113 on the Physical Fitness Index test is a high score, as 115 is the third quartile for normal populations.

Procedures

In the initial pack-carrying study, the physical condition of the subjects might logically have been a factor in the strength decrement results from the pack-carrying marches. Inasmuch as each subject executed a set performance (marching 7.5 miles at a rate of 2.5 miles in 50 minutes), improved condition could be reflected in less strength loss. Had the performance been competitive (i.e., to march the course in the shortest possible time), the SDI's could have remained much the same, with improved condition being expressed in faster time. In fact, this latter hypothesis has been verified in a swimming experiment conducted at the University of Oregon to be considered later in this chapter.

Therefore, because physical conditioning of the subjects resulting from repeated marches was uncontrolled in the initial research, a second study was undertaken which attempted to neutralize this effect on pack-carrying evaluation. Two of the former packs were included: the combat pack carried high on the back and the rucksack. In addition, a Quartermaster experimental pack, designed to locate most of the weight around the waist, was included.

All weights were 41 lbs. As before, the marching distance was 7.5 miles and the rate of march was 2.5 miles in 50 minutes. The subjects were 40 Springfield College students. Significant t ratios for this N are 1.68 at the .05 level and 2.42 at the .01 level. The strength tests utilized, listed in their order of administration, were: shoulder elevation, neck extension, knee flexion, knee extension, hip flexion, hip extension, trunk flexion, and trunk extension.

The conditioning effect on the strength decrement of the muscles resulting from the marches was equalized by employment of the following Latin-square distribution, with the subjects divided into three groups of 13, 13, and 14 subjects, designated A, B, and C:

March	*Combat Pack*	*Rucksack*	*Experimental Pack*
First	A	B	C
Second	B	C	A
Third	C	A	B

Results

The mean strength decrements following the three marches under the respective pack-carrying conditions are summarized in Table 5.4. Both the SDI's and the t ratios for the difference between pre-march means and the means for the greatest SDI during the march are presented. Observations of the strength losses occurring on the various marches are as follows:

1. Carrying the 41-lb. load by means of the QM experimental pack resulted in the least over-all strength loss of the muscle groups tested; the total of the t ratios was 10.96. Only two muscle groups were significantly affected in this march at the .05 level: the trunk extensors with a t ratio of 2.22 (8.43% loss); and hip extensors with a t ratio of 1.97 (6.2% loss).

2. With the combat pack carried high, five muscle groups exhibited significant losses in strength, four of which were beyond the

Table 5.4

SUMMARIZATION OF STRENGTH DECREMENT INDICES
FOR THREE PACK-CARRYING MARCHES

Muscle Group	Combat Pack		Experimental Pack		Rucksack	
	SDI	t	SDI	t	SDI	t
Shoulder elevators	8.99	2.68	6.03	1.54	4.35	1.86
Neck extensors	11.25	4.19	3.72	0.88	7.53	3.11
Knee flexors	9.38	2.62	6.60	1.13	10.59	3.46
Knee extensors	5.85	1.21	2.09	0.65	7.28	2.31
Hip flexors	1.42	0.60	3.60	1.18	4.35	2.12
Hip extensors	4.59	1.80	6.20	1.97	3.88	2.39
Trunk flexors	2.16	0.70	4.15	1.39	7.73	3.81
Trunk extensors	6.40	2.94	8.43	2.22	9.12	2.19

.05 level. The muscle groups were: neck extensors with a t ratio of 4.19 (11.25% loss); trunk extensors with a t ratio of 2.94 (6.40% loss); shoulder elevators with a t ratio of 2.68 (8.99% loss); knee flexors with a t ratio of 2.62 (9.38% loss); and hip extensors with a t ratio for 1.80 (4.59% loss). The total t ratio was 16.74, which is 53 per cent greater than for the experimental pack.

3. In this series, the march with the rucksack resulted in the greatest percentage of loss, approximately twice as much as for the experimental pack and about 25 per cent greater than for the combat pack. All eight muscle groups tested were significantly affected by strength losses.

4. The hip flexors and the trunk extensors were the only muscle groups significantly affected on all three experimental marches. Those muscle groups with significant differences on two marches were: shoulder elevators, neck extensors, and knee flexors.

5. The neck extensor muscle group was added to the battery of strength tests in this study, due to discomfort in this area experienced by the subjects in the earlier series. Considerable stress on these muscles was found for the combat pack and the rucksack, with t ratios of 4.19 (11.25%) and 3.11 (7.53%) respectively. For the QM experimental pack, however, the strain on this muscle group was negligible (t ratio of .88).

Comments on Pack-Carrying Studies

Discussion

Two independent pack-carrying studies were conducted in which were determined strength decrements on selected muscle groups during and following 7.5-mile military marches. In the first study, data were obtained following an exploratory march and six experimental marches. During these marches, the subjects improved considerably in the strength of the muscles tested and on motor-physical fitness tests. No control of this factor was exercised, so that the conditioning benefits from the marches favored the last ones, in which the rucksack was used. In the second study, the conditioning effect was equalized by employment of a Latin-square distribution. However, only three marches were held in this series, so the subjects did not achieve conditioning improvement to the same degree as in the first study. In fact, the condition of these subjects from marching was about at the level of the first experimental march (actually the second march) of the first series.

In the first series of marches, the rucksack had a clear advantage in carrying military loads; not until the weight was 61 lbs. were strength losses appreciable. Contrarily, in the second series, marching with the rucksack resulted in greater strength losses than with the combat pack, both loads being 41 lbs. The difference is attributed to the condition of the subjects on the two marches as discussed above. This contention is further supported by the observation that the SDI's for the rucksack march with 61 lbs., when the subjects were in their best marching condition, are comparable to the SDI's for the rucksack with 41 lbs., when the subjects were unconditioned for marching. For the second series of marches, the QM experimental pack was clearly superior, resulting in considerably less strength decrement for men marching 7.5 miles with a 41-lb. load.

In the first series of marches, the shoulder elevator muscles did not show a significant strength loss when the combat pack was carried high on the back; in the second series, the loss of strength in these muscles was significant beyond the .05 level. The subjects were in about the same stage of marching condition. This discrepancy can be explained by the order in which the strength tests were administered after marching: in the first series, these muscles were tested last, thus permitting about eight minutes of recovery time; in the second series, they were tested first, with very little rest. Other, similar discrepancies in SDI differences between the two series arise from like situations.

A listing of the muscle groups most seriously affected by strength losses (*t* ratios of 3.00 and over) on the various marches in the two series is as follows:

First Series
29-lb. high combat pack: knee flexors (13.78%).
41-lb. high combat pack: knee flexors (13.01%) and knee extensors (5.48%).
41-lb. low combat pack: shoulder elevators (10.28%) and knee flexors (10.30%).
No load: none.
41-lb. rucksack: none.
61-lb. rucksack: trunk flexors (8.08%) and trunk extensors (14.64%).

Second Series
41-lb. high combat pack: neck extensors (11.25%).
41-lb. rucksack: trunk flexors (7.73%), knee flexors (10.59%), and neck extensors (7.53%).
41-lb. QM experimental pack: none

The muscle groups showing greatest strength losses for the nine marches in the two series were: trunk extensors in eight marches; hip extensors in seven marches; and knee flexors in six marches. The ankle plantar flexors were included in the first series only; as they showed significant strength losses on all six of these marches, it is safe to classify them among the frequently affected muscles. The neck extensors appeared in two of the three marches in the second series, but were not tested in series one. Of the other muscle groups, the trunk flexors and the hip flexors were significantly affected in five marches each; the shoulder elevators and knee extensors in four each.

Conclusions

Observations on the strength losses resulting from the various marches with military packs performed in this study are as follows:

1. Military marches with the Quartermaster experimental pack resulted in the least muscular fatigue, as reflected in Strength Decrement Indices of the muscle groups involved. Strength losses in only two muscle groups, trunk extensors and hip extensors, were significant.

2. In the second series of marches, when the subjects were unconditioned for marching, the combat pack carried high on the back was superior to the rucksack. Three muscle groups were significantly affected by strength loss with this pack: neck extensors, trunk extensors, and shoulder elevators.

3. When conditioned, the subjects experienced much less strength loss in marching with military packs, as indicated by the lower Strength Decrement Indices resulting from the seventh march of the first series. On this march, each subject carried a rucksack with a 61-lbs. load. All of the muscle groups tested, except the knee extensors, experienced significant strength losses from this march, with the trunk flexors and extensors having the greatest proportionate loss.

4. Very little difference in over-all strength loss resulted from carrying the combat pack high or low on the back. However, the muscles affected differed somewhat: the shoulder elevators had greater loss with the low pack; and the knee flexors and extensors, with the high pack.

Evaluation of Army Footgear

In addition to the pack and its location on the body in marching, a problem of importance to personal comfort and fatigue in marching or hiking is the type of footgear worn. This investigation was designed to compare the strength loss effects on the muscles of the lower leg and foot resulting from three types of Army boots and shoes worn on an identical pack-carrying march (41).

Procedures

The research procedures applied in this investigation were similar to those described above for the evaluation of Army packs. Thus, only the procedures peculiar to this study will be given here, as follows:

1. The following types of Army footwear were included in the study: combat boot, rubber insulated boot, and quarter-cut shoe. The subjects completed three marches, wearing a different type of boot or shoe each time. The conditioning effect on the strength of the muscles from repeated marches was equalized by employment of a Latin-square distribution.

2. The marching distance and the rate of march was the same as for the pack-carrying studies.

3. The same load of 41 pounds was carried on all three marches. The subjects were dressed in accordance with Army regulations, and the load was distributed on the person as it would be carried in the field. Thus, the pack was located high on the back.

4. The subjects were 29 Springfield College students majoring in physical education. They ranged in age from 18 to 26 years. The following median scores will further describe this group: height, 69 in.; weight, 155 lbs.; Physical Fitness Index, 107; Strength Index, 2900.

5. The cable-tension strength tests were administered in the same order, from weak to strong movements, as follows: ankle inverters, ankle everters, ankle dorsi flexors, and ankle plantar flexors.

6. The usual strength decrements were computed for each 2.5 miles of marching. For 29 subjects, the significant t ratio for a one-tail test is 1.70 at the .05 level.

Results

ANKLE INVERTERS. The Strength Decrement Indices obtained on the marches for the ankle inverter muscles are shown in Fig. 5.3. Observations on these results are:

1. The march in which combat boots were worn had the least effect on strength loss of this muscle group. In fact, strength scores increased at 2.5 and 5.0 miles; and had just reached their pre-march mean at 7.5 miles.

2. With rubber insulated boots, the subjects did not experience fatigue of these muscles at 2.5 miles. However, fatigue increased for the balance of the march (almost a straight-line) to a strength loss of 9.5 per cent. The difference between the pre-march mean and the mean at 7.5 miles was 3.2 lbs.; the *t* ratio was 1.97, which is significant beyond the .05 level.

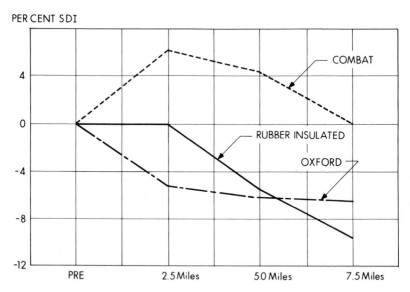

PER CENT SDI

Fig. 5.3   Ankle inversion mean SDI's footwear experiment

3. For the quarter-cut shoes, fatigue of the ankle inverter muscles was felt within the first 2.5 miles, a strength loss of 5.0 per cent. Little change was noted during the remainder of the march. The *t* ratio for the difference between the pre- and post-march strength means was 2.11, indicating significance beyond the .05 level.

ANKLE EVERTERS. The SDI's for the ankle everter muscles on the three footwear marches appear in Fig. 5.4. Comments on these results are:

1. Wearing of the rubber insulated boots resulted in the least strength loss for these muscles; there was a slight increase in strength at 2.5 miles, at which point a steady decline followed for the balance of the march. At 7.5 miles, the SDI approached but did not reach the .05 level of significance (*t* ratio of 1.62).

2. With the combat boot, the decline in strength at 5.0 miles was significant at the .05 level; the *t* ratio was 1.77.

3. The quarter-cut shoe caused by far the greatest strength loss for the ankle everter muscles at 7.5 miles. The SDI was 11.5, with a *t* ratio of 3.72, which was significant beyond the .05 level.

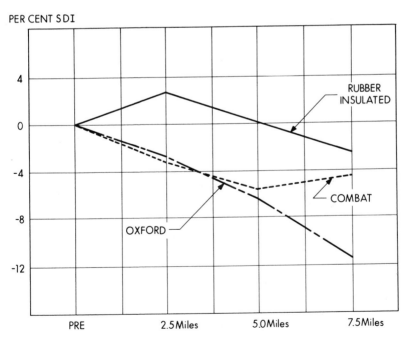

Fig. 5.4 Ankle inversion mean SDI's footwear experiment

ANKLE DORSI FLEXORS. None of the strength decrements of the ankle dorsi flexors on the three marches were significant. In fact, they maintained their pre-march strength throughout.

ANKLE PLANTAR FLEXORS. The SDI's obtained on the marches for the plantar flexor muscles appear in Fig. 5.5. Appropriate observations are:

1. No stress on these muscles was noticeable at 2.5 miles for any of the three types of footwear. At 7.5 miles, however, significant mean strength losses were found with the rubber insulated boot and the quarter-cut shoe; the respective *t* ratios were 1.84 and 1.89, both being significant beyond the .05 level.

2. The loss in strength of the ankle plantar muscles for the march in which combat boots were worn was not significant (*t* ratio

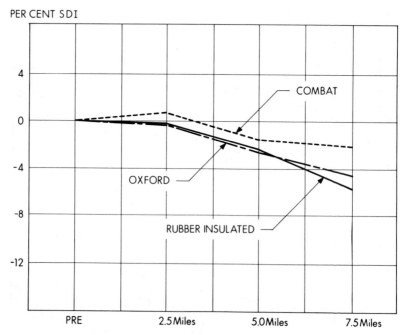

Fig. 5.5 Ankle plantar flexion footwear experiment

of 1.37). These results are not in agreement with those of the pack-carrying study, where strength losses of these muscles were significant for all six marches of the first series. However, the differences between the two series are within the range of chance probability.

Summary and Conclusions

A general summarization of strength decrements for the three marches with different Army footwear appears in Table 5.5. Inasmuch as mean strength losses of the ankle dorsi flexor muscles were not found for any of the marches, this group is omitted from the table. Both the mean SDI's and the *t* ratios for the differences between pre- and post-march strength means are given for each muscle group on each march.

Table 5.5

SUMMARIZATION OF STRENGTH DECREMENT INDICES
FOR THREE FOOTWEAR MARCHES

Footwear March	Mean	*Ankle Inverters*	*Ankle Everters*	*Ankle Plantar Flexors*	*Totals*
Combat boot	SDI	0.00	5.39	3.21	8.60
	t	0.00	1.77	1.37	3.14
Rubber insulated boot	SDI	9.43	2.41	5.61	17.45
	t	1.97	1.62	1.84	5.43
Quarter-cut shoe	SDI	6.40	11.64	4.55	22.59
	t	2.11	3.72	1.89	7.72
Totals	SDI	15.83	19.44	13.37	48.64
	t	4.08	7.11	5.10	16.29

Observations on the strength losses resulting from the various marches performed in this study are as follows:

1. Military marches in combat boots resulted in the least fatigue of the muscles of the lower leg and ankle, as reflected in Strength Decrement Indices of these muscle groups. The lowest total SDI (8.60) was obtained for this march. Only mean strength loss in one muscle group, the ankle everters, was significant at the .05 level.

2. The rubber insulated boot was the next favored of the army footwear studied. The total strength loss for subjects wearing these boots was approximately twice the amount for the march with the combat boot. All three muscle groups showed strength losses which were significant at the .05 level or nearly so.

3. Strength loss with the quarter-cut shoe was the greatest of the three marches. The total strength loss was over two and one-half times as great as for the combat-boot march; and approximately 30 per cent greater than for the march in the rubber insulated boots. The strength losses for two muscle groups, ankle inverters and ankle plantar flexors, were significant beyond the .05 level; and the loss for one, the ankle everters, beyond the .01 level.

4. The muscle group most affected by proportionate strength losses for the three footwear marches was the ankle everters. Significance was found for the different marches as follows: rubber insulated boot, nearly at the .05 level; combat boot, slightly beyond the .05 level; and quarter-cut shoes, beyond the .01 level.

Strength Decrement from Swimming

Procedures

At the University of Oregon, Davis (44) studied, among other things, the Strength Decrement Indices resulting from swimming 200 yards for time. Six muscle groups were tested: shoulder flexion and extension, hip flexion and extension, and knee flexion and extension.

SDI's for these muscle groups were obtained on the occasion of the subjects' first swimming time trials, when unconditioned, and, again, after five weeks of training for the 200-yard swim, when in a conditioned state. Every effort was made to speed up this process after the swim in order to reduce to a minimum the strength recovery time of the muscle groups being tested. The order of administering the post-swim strength tests was rotated in accordance with a Latin-square procedure so that the time necessarily allowed for strength recovery was equalized for all muscle groups.

Results

The SDI's for the first and last 200-yard swim time trials appear in Table 5.6. The differences between the SDI means on these time trials were not significant; the highest *t* ratios were 1.37 and 1.33 for the shoulder extensors and the hip flexors. The over-all strength loss was 2.2 per cent less on the last swim. Thus, the effects of these all-out exertions were nearly the same for both first and last trials.

Table 5.6

MEAN STRENGTH DECREMENT INDICES OF COLLEGE MEN
OBTAINED FROM SWIMMING 200 YARDS FOR TIME

Test	First Time Trial	Last Time Trial	Differences Between Means	t Ratio
Shoulder flexors	14.33	11.11	−3.22	0.93
Shoulder extensors	22.23	18.23	−4.00	1.37
Hip flexors	17.63	8.79	−8.84	1.33
Hip extensors	12.04	14.86	2.82	0.54
Knee flexors	12.99	12.46	−0.53	0.10
Knee extensors	6.97	7.54	0.57	0.16
Mean SDI	14.37	12.17	−2.20	0.89

At first glance, it may seem strange that five weeks of conditioning did not produce changes in the muscle fatigue situation. More specifically, why did not the muscles fatigue less on the last swim? This may be explained by the fact that the subjects swam all-out on both time trials, so that approximately the same amount of muscular fatigue occurred each time. If fatigue is of a certain magnitude, loss in applicable muscular strength is in proportion. Inasmuch as the mean time decreased by 23.7 seconds between the two swims, conditioning was reflected by improved swimming time rather than reduced muscular fatigue; in other words, the subjects swam faster for the same degree of muscular fatigue.

The greatest SDI's on the two swims were found for the shoulder extensor muscles, the muscles directly responsible for the propulsive phase of the arm stroke; the indices were 22.23 and 18.23. The smallest SDI's were obtained for the knee extensor muscles (6.97 and 7.54). The other SDI's ranged from 8.79 to 17.63.

Treadmill Running

Procedures

This study (25) was undertaken to examine the fatigue effects in muscles of the trunk and lower extremities induced by a submaximal run on a treadmill. The strength decrements of the following 14 muscle groups were obtained: trunk flexors and extensors; hip flexors, extensors, abductors, adductors, inward rotators, and outward rotators; knee flexors and extensors; and ankle dorsi flexors, plantar flexors, inverters, and everters. Post-exercise cable-tension strength tests were taken one minute after completion of the treadmill run.

The specified run on the treadmill was at seven miles per hour for a period of ten minutes on a horizontal plane. These conditions were selected as submaximal, allowing all of the subjects to complete the run, but were strenuous enough to cause a moderate to a high state of fatigue. This determination was based on several trial runs at various speeds and distances by laboratory personnel and random volunteers. Subjects who were unable to complete the specified run were eliminated from the study.

The subjects were male university students. Strength decrements were obtained on 17 subjects for each of the 14 muscle groups. Thus, 238 different subjects participated in the study.

For 17 subjects, a *t* ratio of 1.75 denotes a significant difference between pre- and post-run means at the .05 level. This value for *t* was chosen because significance was measured from zero, or no difference, in one direction only; as demonstrated repeatedly, muscular fatigue will decrease (not increase) strength.

Table 5.7

MEAN STRENGTH DECREMENTS OF 14 MUSCLE GROUPS
FROM SUBMAXIMAL TREADMILL RUNNING

Test	M_1*	M_2†	M_d	σd	t *ratio*
1. Trunk flexion	133.41	124.17	−9.24	3.09	2.99
2. Trunk extension	111.44	113.68	2.24	6.22	0.36
3. Hip flexion	150.79	153.55	2.76	0.81	0.90
4. Hip extension	128.25	132.23	3.98	4.25	0.94
5. Hip abduction	149.01	147.96	−1.05	2.73	0.38
6. Hip adduction	114.90	114.59	−0.31	1.19	0.26
7. Hip inward rotation	30.52	29.37	−1.15	1.53	0.76
8. Hip outward rotation	47.03	43.74	−3.29	0.91	3.61
9. Knee flexion	163.91	158.04	−5.87	4.03	1.46
10. Knee extension	272.06	265.00	−7.06	8.28	0.85
11. Ankle inversion	30.78	29.94	−0.84	0.77	1.09
12. Ankle eversion	63.09	65.29	2.20	1.90	1.17
13. Ankle dorsi flexion	91.25	91.73	0.48	3.50	0.14
14. Ankle plantar flexion	374.90	372.90	−2.00	8.99	0.22

* Pre-exercise mean.

† Post-exercise mean.

Results

The results of this research appear in Table 5.7. Appropriate interpretations are as follows:

1. The highest t ratios were 3.61 and 2.99, obtained for strength decrements of the hip outward rotator and trunk flexor muscles respectively; these drops were significant beyond the .05 level. Thus, these muscle groups showed the greatest muscular fatigue as a result of the prescribed treadmill run.

2. No other differences between the strength decrement means were significant. The highest of the remaining t ratios was 1.46 for the knee flexors.

Judging from results of this study, the muscular fatigue effects on the different subjects depended on their level of physical condition, inasmuch as the treadmill run was set at a prescribed speed and length of time. Some subjects completed the run easily while others were under obvious stress at the end. Thus, the strength decrement effect varied from subject to subject; it was not essentially constant as in the all-out swimming efforts reported above.

Summary

The studies reported in this chapter demonstrate that the Strength Decrement Index can be used effectively to evaluate the muscular fatigue effects resulting from physical activity. The experimental situations involved pack-carrying on military marches, all-out swimming for time, and a submaximal treadmill run. Summaries and conclusions of the results are given at the ends of the various reports, so will not be repeated here.

Chapter 6

Muscular Strength and Fatigue Relationships

In this chapter, various muscular strength and fatigue relationships will be presented. In the main, only muscular strength relationships involving the cable-tension type of strength testing will be included. For muscular fatigue relationships, mostly studies in strength decrement are reported. These restrictions are in harmony with the other research reported in this monograph where cable-tension strength tests and strength decrement evaluations were also utilized.

Intercorrelations of Cable-Tension Strength Tests

Most of the intercorrelations of the strengths of various muscle groups throughout the body reported in this section were obtained from the Medford, Oregon, Boys' Growth Project (31). This project is an ongoing longitudinal investigation in which the same boys are tested annually from ages 7 to 18 years; during the first year of the study, however, cross-sectional data were obtained with independent samples at each age from 9 to 15 years inclusive. The over-all purposes of the project

141

are as follows: to study the physical and motor growth patterns and the individual differences of boys 7 to 18 years of age; to compare the physical and motor growth characteristics of boys at different levels of athletic ability; and to determine relationships between physical, motor, personal-social, and mental qualities of boys at these ages. Among the measures included in this project are cable-tension strength tests, selected to sample the various muscles of the body. As a consequence, relationship analyses with these tests became possible.

Elementary School Boys

The most comprehensive intercorrelational study of cable-tension strength tests was conducted by Schopf (82), also reported by Clarke and Schopf (36). The subjects were 128 Medford elementary school boys in grades four, five, and six. Eighteen cable-tension strength tests covering the major muscle groups of the body were included.

INTERCORRELATIONS. The intercorrelation coefficients for the strengths of the 18 muscle groups appear in Table 6.1. A coefficient of .227 denotes significance at the .01 level. Observations justified from these results follow:

1. In general, the product-moment correlations were relatively high. Of the 153 intercorrelations among the 18 cable-tension strength tests, all were significant near or beyond the .01 level. These correlations ranged from .223 to .809.

2. The strength tests with the highest correlations with the others were shoulder extension, shoulder adduction, hip abduction, knee extension, and ankle plantar flexion. The strength tests with lowest intercorrelations with the others were elbow extension, hip inward rotation, and ankle dorsal flexion.

3. The highest correlations between strength tests were: .809 between trunk flexion and trunk extension, .800 between shoulder extension and shoulder adduction, .776 between shoulder adduction and ankle plantar flexion, .764 between knee extension and ankle plantar flexion, .761 between shoulder adduction and knee extension, and .753 between hip flexion and hip extension.

Table 6.1

INTERCORRELATIONS BETWEEN INDIVIDUAL CABLE-TENSION STRENGTH TESTS AND THE AVERAGE STRENGTH CRITERION* FOR BOYS NINE THROUGH TWELVE YEARS OF AGE

	Elbo Flex 1	Elbo Ext 2	Shdr Flex 3	Shdr Ext 4	Shdr Add 5	Shdr I Rot 6	Neck Ext 7	Trnk Flex 8	Trnk Ext 9	Hip Flex 10	Hip Ext 11	Hip Add 12	Hip Abd 13	Hip I Rot 14	Knee Flex 15	Knee Ext 16	Ankle D Flx 17	Ankle P Flx 18
C*	.803	.519	.754	.889	.868	.714	.731	.796	.795	.727	.791	.659	.795	.663	.746	.859	.628	.844
1	—	.459	.628	.686	.607	.598	.592	.605	.612	.574	.599	.645	.615	.556	.521	.606	.586	.628
2		—	.487	.466	.381	.391	.410	.314	.338	.319	.339	.307	.412	.349	.223	.293	.331	.394
3			—	.675	.593	.577	.599	.460	.537	.479	.522	.538	.551	.529	.473	.619	.476	.574
4				—	.800	.690	.661	.696	.659	.701	.701	.639	.738	.498	.582	.734	.578	.705
5					—	.531	.635	.643	.654	.665	.657	.564	.676	.436	.641	.761	.464	.776
6						—	.456	.534	.502	.503	.575	.428	.539	.459	.426	.558	.496	.542
7							—	.527	.549	.547	.474	.462	.520	.378	.594	.629	.390	.604
8								—	.809	.622	.586	.506	.600	.509	.537	.657	.399	.607
9									—	.568	.553	.394	.573	.465	.546	.581	.448	.583
10										—	.753	.490	.526	.506	.585	.663	.426	.629
11											—	.551	.634	.511	.621	.673	.537	.596
12												—	.575	.531	.460	.579	.394	.554
13													—	.550	.499	.653	.531	.726
14														—	.453	.473	.517	.551
15															—	.730	.410	.613
16																—	.461	.764
17																	—	.443
18																		—

* Average strength criterion: Average of 18 cable-tension strength tests.

4. Frequently, the strength correlations between muscles that are antagonists or are in the same joint area were among the highest obtained. For example: trunk flexion vs. extension (.809), shoulder extension vs. adduction (.800), hip flexion vs. extension (.753), knee flexion vs. extension (.730), shoulder extension vs. inward rotation (.690), shoulder flexion vs. extension (.675), and hip extension vs. abduction (.634). Exceptions to this phenomenon involved the knee extensor and the ankle plantar flexor muscles; the strength of these muscle groups correlated well with each other (.761) and with a number of other tests.

5. The lowest intercorrelations were with elbow extension strength, as follows: .223 with knee flexion, .293 with knee extension, .307 with hip adduction, .314 with trunk flexion, and .319 with hip flexion. The highest correlation with elbow extension strength was .487; shoulder flexion was the other strength test.

MULTIPLE CORRELATION. A criterion measure was established which consisted of the average of the 18 cable-tension strength tests. In computing each subject's average, his 18 strength test scores were added directly, instead of transforming them first to standard scores. In this way, the strength of each muscle group contributed its proportionate share to the criterion, the stronger muscles more than the weaker muscles.

In Table 6.1, the C row contains the correlation coefficients of the 18 strength tests with the criterion measure. These coefficients ranged from .519 with elbow extension to .889 with shoulder extension strength. The highest correlations, listed in descending order, were as follows:

.889 shoulder extension	.796 trunk flexion
.868 shoulder adduction	.795 trunk extension
.859 knee extension	.795 hip abduction
.844 ankle plantar flexion	.791 hip extension
.803 elbow flexion	

A coefficient of multiple correlation was computed by the Wherry-Doolittle method of test selection (51). The criterion was the dependent variable and the 18 strength tests were the independent variables. While the resultant multiple correlation is spuriously high, since the strength tests compose the criterion measure, this process does identify the minimum significant variables in the total situation. The development of the multiple correlation was as follows:

Strength Test	r with Criterion	Multiple Correlation
Shoulder Extension	.889	
Ankle Plantar Flexion	.844	.940
Trunk Extension	.795	.964
Knee Extension	.859	.976

The four tests selected by the multiple correlation process represent almost equally strong movements. Further, they all measure the strength of extension movements of the joints involved (ankle plantar flexion is, in fact, ankle extension).

STRENGTH TEST NORMS. Strength test norms were constructed for the total score on the four cable-tension strength tests, selected as described above by multiple correlation method. The subjects were 826 boys in grades four, five, and six from ten public schools located throughout Oregon; the subjects were selected at random within each school.

The procedures adopted by Rogers (81) in the construction of Strength Index norms to obtain the Physical Fitness Index were adopted. The essential norm construction process was the determination of the increase associated with an increase in weight for a given age; a double-entry table containing the amounts of strength for various ages (by half years) and weights (by two-pound increments) was the final result. These norms appear in Schopf's study (82), or may be obtained from the author of this monograph.

Junior High School Boys

Tomaras (86) studied the relationships of anthropometric and strength measures of Medford junior high school boys, aged 12 through 14 years, to various arm strength criteria. Among his variables were seven cable-tension strength tests involving the arm and shoulder muscles. For these muscle groups, therefore, it was possible to compare the intercorrelations obtained from junior high school boys with those obtained from upper elementary school boys, as presented above. Inasmuch as the muscle groups in Tomaras's study were limited to the arm and shoulder girdle region, the intercorrelations among 12 muscle groups located throughout the body were computed for this study of junior high school boys.

Comparisons of the intercorrelations for 12 strength tests obtained by Schopf for upper elementary grades and those especially computed for junior high school boys are presented in Table 6.2. The difference between each pair of correlations was tested for significance: each pair of correlation coefficients were converted to Fisher Z coefficients; a *t* ratio was computed for the difference between Z coefficients. A significant *t* ratio at the .05 level for 239 degrees of freedom is 1.97.

Whenever differences between pairs of intercorrelations were significant, the correlations for the junior high schools boys were highest; this was true for the correlations appearing in Table 6.2 and for the correlations obtained by Tomaras. For three muscle groups, none of the differences between correlations were significant; these strength tests were for knee extension, ankle dorsi flexion, and ankle plantar flexion. Observations pertaining to the significant differences between strength intercorrelations follow.

ELBOW FLEXION STRENGTH. The differences between elbow flexion strength intercorrelations with shoulder flexion, hip flexion, and hip extension strengths were significant (Table 6.2); the respective *t* ratios were 3.00, 3.23, and 2.40. In Tomaras's study, significant correlation differences for this muscle group were also found with elbow extension, shoulder adduction, and neck extension strength; the *t* ratios were 4.72, 2.80, and 3.43, respectively.

ELBOW EXTENSION STRENGTH. In Tomaras's study, the junior high school boys had significantly higher intercorrelations with elbow extension strength than did the upper elementary school boys for five muscle groups. The five strength tests with *t* ratios were: elbow extension (4.72), shoulder adduction (4.07), shoulder inward rotation (3.72), shoulder flexion (2.80), and shoulder extension (2.72).

SHOULDER FLEXION STRENGTH. For shoulder flexion strength (Table 6.2), the intercorrelations with elbow flexion and hip flexion strengths were significantly higher for the junior high school boys; the *t* ratios were 3.00 and 3.62 respectively. In addition, the difference in correlations between shoulder flexion and hip extension strengths for the two groups of boys approached significance at the .05 level, since the *t* ratio was 1.92. As reported above, the correlations with this muscle group in Tomaras's study was also significantly higher for elbow flexion and elbow extension strengths.

HIP FLEXION STRENGTH. As shown in Table 6.2, three of the differences between intercorrelations with hip flexion strength were significant. The three muscle groups with *t* ratios were shoulder flexion (3.62), elbow flexion (3.23), and shoulder inward rotation (2.15). In addition, the difference in correlations between hip flexion and hip extension strengths nearly reached significance at the .05 level, since the *t* ratio was 1.92.

HIP INWARD ROTATION STRENGTH. As shown in Table 6.2, three of the differences between intercorrelations with hip inward rotation strength were significant. The three muscle groups with *t* ratios were trunk flexion (2.47), knee flexion (2.23), and trunk extension (2.08).

Same-Age Boys

In computing the intercorrelations of strength tests reported above for upper elementary and junior high school boys, it was noted that chronological age varied by as much as three years in each group. Inasmuch as muscular strength increases with age, possibly the presence of chronological age as a third factor in the correlations served to increase their magnitude.

As a consequence, the intercorrelations for boys of the same age, 13 years, with boys tested within two months of their birthdays, were

Table 6.2

STRENGTH TEST INTERCORRELATION COMPARISONS BETWEEN
UPPER ELEMENTARY AND JUNIOR HIGH SCHOOL BOYS

	Shdr Flex	Shdr Inv	Trunk Flex	Trunk Ext	Hip Flex	Hip Ext	Hip Inw	Knee Flex	Knee Ext	Ankle Dorsi	Ankle Plantar
Elbow Flexion											
Elem. School	.63	.60	.61	.61	.57	.60	.56	.52	.61	.59	.63
Jr. High School	.82	.80	.58	.50	.79	.76	.44	.54	.73	.67	.53
t Ratio	3.00*	1.38	0.40	1.23	3.23*	2.40*	1.23	0.15	1.78	1.00	1.15
Shoulder Flexion											
Elem. School		.58	.46	.54	.48	.52	.53	.47	.62	.48	.57
Jr. High School		.65	.59	.54	.71	.68	.51	.48	.69	.61	.54
t Ratio		0.92	1.46	0.00	3.62*	1.92	0.23	0.08	0.92	1.46	0.38
Shoulder Inward Rotation											
Elem. School			.53	.50	.50	.58	.46	.43	.56	.50	.54
Jr. High School			.55	.61	.68	.67	.36	.58	.68	.51	.53
t Ratio			0.24	1.23	2.15*	1.15	0.92	1.54	1.54	0.08	0.08
Trunk Flexion											
Elem. School				.81	.62	.58	.51	.54	.66	.40	.61
Jr. High School				.74	.68	.65	.24*	.45	.61	.41	.56
t Ratio				1.38	0.92	0.92	2.47*	0.93	1.39	0.08	0.62
Trunk Extension											
Elem. School					.57	.55	.47	.55	.58	.45	.58
Jr. High School					.60	.61	.24*	.48	.61	.28	.59
t Ratio					0.31	0.69	2.08*	0.62	0.39	1.23	0.15
Hip Flexion											
Elem. School						.75	.51	.59	.66	.43	.63
Jr. High School						.84	.38	.59	.76	.60	.61
t Ratio						1.92	1.23	0.00	1.62	1.76	0.23

	Shdr Flex	Shdr Inv	Trunk Flex	Trunk Ext	Hip Flex	Hip Ext	Hip Inw	Knee Flex	Knee Ext	Ankle Dorsi	Ankle Plantar
Hip Extension											
Elem. School							.51	.62	.67	.54	.60
Jr. High School							.36	.59	.75	.60	.66
t Ratio							1.38	0.38	1.20	0.69	0.78
Hip Inward Rotation											
Elem. School								.45	.47	.52	.55
Jr. High School								.21	.41	.48	.40
t Ratio								2.23*	0.53	0.46	1.54
Knee Flexion											
Elem. School									.73	.41	.61
Jr. High School									.66	.38	.52
t Ratio									1.08	0.31	1.00
Knee Extension											
Elem. School										.46	.76
Jr. High School										.61	.70
t Ratio										1.62	1.00
Ankle Dorsi Flexion											
Elem. School											.44
Jr. High School											.43
t Ratio											0.08

* Significant at or above .05 level.

made in a study from the Medford growth project by Burt (6). These were compared with the intercorrelations obtained from the junior high school boys as reported in Table 6.2. Cable-tension strength tests for the same 12 muscle groups were available in both studies; thus, comparisons of 66 pairs of intercorrelations were possible. The difference between the correlations composing each pair was tested for significance by application of the t ratio to the difference between their corresponding Fisher Z coefficients. Significant t ratio for 213 degrees of freedom is 1.97 at the .05 level.

Only 5 of the 66 differences between the paired intercorrelations were significant at the .05 level. In all instances, the junior high school boys as a group had higher correlations than did the 13-year-old boys. For the five significant differences between correlations, either elbow flexion or knee extension strength tests were involved. The paired correlations for these significant differences with t ratios are as follows:

	Correlations		
Muscle Groups	Jr. High School	13-Yr.-Olds	t Ratios for Diff.
Elbow Flexion vs. Shoulder Flexion	.82	.38	4.47
Elbow Flexion vs. Hip Flexion	.79	.55	2.65
Elbow Flexion vs. Knee Extension	.73	.52	2.06
Knee Extension vs. Shoulder Flexion	.62	.33	2.29
Knee Extension vs. Trunk Flexion	.66	.41	2.06

Correlations Between Cable-Tension Strength Tests and Physical-Motor Fitness Measures

Arm Strength Measures (21)

JUNIOR HIGH SCHOOL BOYS. In a study of 100 Medford junior high school boys, Tomaras (86) related seven cable-tension strength tests to five arm strength measures. The cable-tension strength tests were elbow flexion and extension, shoulder flexion, extension, adduction, and inward rotation, and neck extension. The four arm strength criteria were as follows:

> Rogers Arm Strength Score:
> [chins + bar dips] × [.1 weight + (height −60)].
> McCloy Pull-Up and Push-Up Scores:
> 1.77 (weight) + 3.42 (chins or bar dips) −46.
> McCloy Athletic Strength Index:
> R + L grips + 2 (Push-Up + Pull-Up Strengths) −3 (weight).
> Composite Cable-Tension Strength:
> Sum of seven cable-tension strength tests, as listed above.

The correlations of the seven strength tests with the five arm strength measures appear in Table 6.3. A correlation of .257 is necessary for significance at the .01 level.

Table 6.3

CORRELATIONS BETWEEN CABLE-TENSION STRENGTH TESTS
AND VARIOUS ARM STRENGTH CRITERIA,
JUNIOR HIGH SCHOOL BOYS

Cable-Tension Strength Test	Arm Strength Measures				
	Rogers Score	McCloy Pull-Ups	McCloy Push-Ups	McCloy Athletic Index	Composite Cl-T Strength
Elbow Flexion	.65	.78	.80	.84	.91
Elbow Extension	.62	.75	.78	.79	.87
Shoulder Flexion	.57	.70	.71	.76	.90
Shoulder Extension	.62	.72	.75	.78	.87
Shoulder Adduction	.75	.74	.78	.81	.90
Shoulder Inward Rotation	.60	.68	.72	.73	.82
Neck Extension	.59	.69	.72	.75	.78

All correlations between the cable-tension strength tests and the arm strength measures were significant well beyond the .01 level. The correlations ranged from .57 to .91. Thus, these single strength measures, the left arm, only, being tested, correlate well with arm strength scores derived from chins and bar dips as related to weight and from strength composites.

The highest correlations were obtained with Strength Composite as the arm strength measure. These results should be expected since the Strength Composite is composed of the tests with which it was correlated; thus, a certain amount of self-correlation is present. The correlations ranged from .78 for neck extension to .91 for elbow flexion strength. A multiple correlation of .992 was obtained with this arm strength measure as the dependent variable; the independent variables were elbow flexion, shoulder extension, shoulder flexion, and shoulder adduction strengths.

The correlations between the cable-tension strength tests and the three McCloy arm strength measures did not vary greatly. The correlational ranges were as follows: Athletic Index, from .73 for shoulder inward rotation to .84 for elbow flexion strength; Push-Up Score, from .71 for shoulder flexion to .80 for elbow flexion strength; and Pull-Up Score, from .68 for shoulder inward rotation to .78 for elbow flexion strength.

With the Rogers Arm Strength Score as the arm strength measure, correlations with the cable-tension strength tests were consistently lower. Their range was from .57 for shoulder flexion to .75 for shoulder adduction strength. With the exception of the Rogers score, elbow flexion strength had the highest correlations with the arm strength measures.

SAME-AGE BOYS. When boys of the same age are used as subjects, the magnitude of correlations between cable-tension strength tests and arm strength measures is reduced. With Medford 12-year-old boys, Degutis (46) obtained a correlation of .54 between elbow flexion strength and the McCloy Arm Strength Score (chins and bar dips combined). This correlation was significantly lower than the .80 obtained by Tomaras with junior high school boys as a group; the t ratio for the difference between the Fisher Z coefficient equivalents of these correlations was 3.33.

With Medford 13-year-old boys, Glines (52), also reported by Clarke and Glines (32), obtained correlations of .22 and .43 between the Rogers Arm Strength Score and shoulder flexion and shoulder inward rotation strengths, respectively. The difference between the Z coefficient equivalents of the shoulder flexion strength correlations of .57 for Tomaras' junior high school boys and the .22 for the 13-year-old boys was significant at the .01 level; the t ratio was 2.63. While the shoulder inward rotation strength correlation of .43 for the 13-year-old boys was lower than the correlation of .60 for the junior high school boys, the difference between the corresponding Z coefficients was not significant, since the t ratio was 1.31.

UNIVERSITY MEN. The correlations between cable-tension strength tests and arm strength measures were lower for university men as shown by Irish (65) than for junior high school boys, as presented above. The comparable correlations are presented in Table 6.4.

The difference between the correlations in each pair in Table 6.4 was tested for significance in the same manner as described above. The significant t ratio is 1.98 at the .05 level.

The range of correlations between strength tests and arm strength measures for junior high school boys was from .57 to .84; for university men, the range was from .23 to .59. While the junior high school boys consistently had higher correlations, they were not all significantly higher. For elbow flexion strength, the junior high school boys had significantly higher correlations with all three arm strength measures; the t ratios ranged from 2.75 to 3.95. Other significant differences between correlations were as follows: shoulder extension, shoulder adduction, and shoulder inward rotation with Rogers Arm Strength Score (t's between 2.05 and 2.25); shoulder extension and shoulder adduction with McCloy Pull-Up Score (t's of 2.00 and 2.15). The difference between shoulder flexion strength and the arm strength scores was not significant.

In an earlier report by Clarke (23), the results of three studies of the relationships of strength and anthropometric tests to various arm strength measures were presented. The subjects were 62 Springfield College men, most of whom were majoring in physical education. The correlations between cable-tension strength tests and the Rogers and McCloy arm strength scores for these college men were

Table 6.4

STRENGTH TEST CORRELATIONS WITH ARM STRENGTH MEASURES
CONTRASTING JUNIOR HIGH SCHOOL BOYS
AND UNIVERSITY MEN

Cable-Tension Strength Test	Arm Strength Measures		
	Rogers Score	McCloy Pull-Ups	McCloy Push-Ups
Elbow Flexion			
Junior High School Boys	.65	.78	.84
University Men	.23	.42	.41
t Ratio	2.75*	3.00*	3.95*
Shoulder Flexion			
Junior High School Boys	.57	.70	.71
University Men	.41	.51	.58
t Ratio	1.05	1.55	1.65
Shoulder Extension			
Junior High School Boys	.62	.72	.75
University Men	.31	.47	.54
t Ratio	2.05*	2.00*	1.85
Shoulder Adduction			
Junior High School Boys	.75	.74	.78
University Men	.49	.48	.58
t Ratio	2.15*	2.15*	1.95
Shoulder Inward Rotation			
Junior High School Boys	.60	.68	.72
University Men	.24	.52	.59
t Ratio	2.25*	1.25	1.15

* Differences significant at or beyond .05 level.

comparable to the correlations obtained for University of Oregon men shown in Table 6.4. The only exceptions pertained to the Rogers Arm Strength Score; the Springfield correlations were significantly lower for three of the strength tests, shoulder flexion, shoulder extension, and shoulder adduction.

Explosive Power

In a study of physical performances involving the trunks and legs of 53 University of Oregon men, Clarke (21) included vertical and standing broad jumps as explosive power tests. The correlations between these jumps and 16 cable-tension strength tests appear in Table 6.5. Also, in this table, correlations are included between standing broad jump distance and five cable-tension strength tests obtained by Degutis (46) with 81 junior high school boys as subjects. Significant correlations at the .05 level are .27 and .22 for the college men and 12-year-old boys respectively.

None of the cable-tension strength tests was significantly correlated with distance in the vertical jump. The highest correlation was −.22 between the jump and trunk lateral flexion strength.

For the university men, a correlation of .30 was obtained between standing broad jump distance and hip extension strength; this correlation is significant at the .05 level. For the junior high school boys, four of the five correlations between the standing broad jump distance and strength measures were significant; the strength measures were elbow flexion, hip extension, ankle plantar flexion, and knee extension.

Table 6.5

CORRELATIONS BETWEEN CABLE-TENSION STRENGTH TESTS
AND THE VERTICAL AND STANDING BROAD JUMPS

Cable-Tension Strength Test	*Vertical Jump*	*Standing Broad Jump*	
		Univ. Men	*12-yr.-Old Boys*
Elbow Flexion			.47*
Trunk Flexion	−.10	−.22	.13
Trunk Extension	.14	−.10	
Trunk Lateral Flexion	−.22	−.22	
Trunk Rotation	.06	.13	
Hip Flexion	.11	.16	
Hip Extension	.15	.30*	.39*
Hip Abduction	−.05	.05	
Hip Adduction	.08	.26	
Hip Outward Rotation	.08	.00	
Hip Inward Rotation	−.10	−.07	
Knee Flexion	−.04	.04	
Knee Extension	−.09	−.04	.28*
Ankle Inversion	.03	−.02	
Ankle Eversion	.16	.19	
Ankle Dorsi Flexion	.00	.11	
Ankle Plantar Flexion	−.05	.01	.32*

* Significant at or beyond the .05 level.

Other Motor Fitness Items

In the study of university men by Clarke (21) previously mentioned correlations between 16 cable-tension strength tests and the following motor fitness items were presented: squat jumps, squat thrusts for one minute, squat thrusts for 12 seconds (original Burpee test), and sit-ups for two minutes. Only one of the 64 correlations was significant at the .05 level; this correlation was .26 between hip adduction strength and squat jumps.

In the study of 13-year-old boys reported by Clarke and Glines (32), also cited before, seven cable-tension strength tests were correlated with a 60-yard shuttle run (10-yard distance). These correlations were as follows:

−.43 Shoulder inward rotation	−.32 Hip flexion
−.41 Hip extension	−.24 Knee flexion
−.36 Knee extension	−.21 Shoulder flexion
−.33 Ankle plantar flexion	

The negative correlations have a positive connotation between speed and strength, as a shorter time for the shuttle run indicates greater speed than a longer time. Five of these correlations reached the .32 needed for significance at the .01 level; the strength tests were shoulder inward rotation, hip extension, knee extension, ankle plantar flexion, and hip flexion. The remaining two correlations approached but did not reach the .25 necessary for significance at the .05 level.

Correlations with Cable-Tension Averages

In a number of the studies mentioned earlier in this chapter, the cable-tension strength tests included were averaged to provide scores indicative of the over-all strength of the musculature involved. As a phase of these studies, the individual muscle groups were related to these averages by zero-order and multiple correlation procedures. While spuriousness exists in these correlational situations, as pointed out before, this process does serve to identify the muscle groups of greatest significance in the total strength pattern. For this reason, it seems desirable to report these results.

In studies previously mentioned in this chapter, the correlations between a cable-tension strength test, as the dependent variable, or criterion, and the various strength tests composing the criterion, as the independent variables, have been reported. In the study of upper elementary school boys by Clarke and Schopf (36, 82), the average of 18 strength tests composed the criterion. Four of the tests correlated .976 with the strength average; these four strength tests were shoulder extension, ankle plantar flexion, trunk extension, and knee extension.

In Tomaras's study (86) of the arm strength of junior high school boys, seven cable-tension strength tests from the arm and shoulder girdle area were averaged. A multiple correlation of .992 was obtained between this criterion and the strengths of the elbow flexor, shoulder extensor, shoulder flexor, and shoulder adductor muscles. In this study, too, three strength tests each correlated .90 to .91 with the strength average; these tests were elbow flexion, shoulder flexion, and shoulder adduction. Further, the following correlations were obtained between Tomaras's arm and shoulder strength test average and the other arm strength measures: .90 with the McCloy Athletic Strength Index; .86 with the McCloy Push-Up Score; .83 with McCloy Pull-Up Score; and .72 with the Rogers Arm Strength Score.

In the study of the reaction, movement, and completion times of 13-year-old boys by Clarke and Glines (32, 52), seven cable-tension strength tests were averaged. The correlations of the individual strength tests with this average for these single-age boys were:

.86 with hip extension	.71 with knee flexion
.85 with ankle plantar flexion	.70 with knee extension
.80 with hip flexion	.59 with shoulder flexion
.76 with shoulder inward rotation	

In addition, a correlation of .81 was obtained between this strength test average and the Rogers Strength Index; the correlation with Rogers Physical Fitness Index was .46. Other correlations with this strength average were .45 with standing broad jump distance and −.30 with 60-yard shuttle run (10-yard distance).

Cable-Tension Strength Related to Maturity

In three studies using data from the Medford Boys' Growth Project, the relationships between various physical and motor factors and the maturity of boys at different ages were examined. In these studies, cable-tension strength tests were included among the experimental variables. Thus, from these studies, some of the relationships between strength and maturation can be reported.

Potential Maturity Indicators

Burt (6) tested the hypothesis that a general factor of physiological maturity exists among 13-year-old boys. Observations were made on 62 subjects who were all within two months of their birthdays.

From a preliminary selection of 51 tests reflecting body dimensions, physique type, strength, and motor ability, a final selection of 33 experimental variables was made; those variables were retained that had a correlation significant at the .05 level with either or both. maturity criteria of skeletal age and pubescent assessment. The intercorrelation coefficients for the tests finally selected were factor analyzed according to the principal-axes method in which communalities represented the largest coefficients found in each row or column of the intercorrelation matrix. The Varimax criterion for rotation was employed to maximize the loadings on each factor and to avoid the *ad hoc* quality of subjective rotation.

Analysis of the data resulted in three principal-axes factors. The first factor was identified as general maturity; this identification was substantiated by the high loadings of skeletal age and pubescent status. Skeletal age was nearly co-linear with this factor $(r = .961)$ and pubescent status had a loading of .681. Further, general maturity accounted for approximately 78 per cent of the common variance of all tests included. In the rotations, three factors were identified; these were named body bulk, maturity lag, and linearity of bone structure.

In the original 51 tests, 12 cable-tension strength tests were included; these tests were selected from muscle groups throughout the body, including those activating the elbow, shoulder, trunk, hip, knee, and ankle joints. All of these tests correlated significantly with the maturity criteria, so were retained for the factor analysis.

MATURITY CORRELATIONS. The correlations of the 12 cable-tension strength tests with skeletal age ranged from .288 for knee flexion to .565 for elbow flexion. For the maturity criterion of pubescent assessment, the lowest correlation was .262 with shoulder flexion and the highest correlation was .597 again with elbow flexion.

GENERAL MATURITY FACTOR. The highest loadings on the general maturity factor were .96 for skeletal age, .90 for chest girth × height, and .86 for weight; no other loading exceeded .79. The loadings of the cable-tension strength tests on this general factor were as follows:

Strength Test	Loading	Strength Test	Loading
Hip Inward Rotation	.77	Knee Extension	.65
Hip Extension	.74	Hip Flexion	.64
Elbow Flexion	.73	Trunk Extension	.60
Ankle Plantar Flexion	.71	Knee Flexion	.60
Trunk Flexion	.69	Shoulder Flexion	.56
Ankle Dorsi Flexion	.68	Shoulder Inward Rotation	.56

MATURITY LAG. All of the 35 variables had negative loadings on the second rotated factor, indicating an inverse relationship between this factor and the variables. The highest loadings on this factor were the strength measures. The loadings of the 12 cable-tension and the other strength tests included in this study were as follows:

Strength Test	Loading	Strength Test	Loading
Hip Extension	−.75	Ankle Dorsi Flexion	−.59
Back Lift	−.71	Knee Extension	−.58
Trunk Flexion	−.71	Shoulder Flexion	−.57
Shoulder Inward Rotation	−.67	Hip Flexion	−.56
Left Grip	−.66	Hip Inward Rotation	−.53
Ankle Plantar Flexion	−.65	Knee Flexion	−.53
Elbow Flexion	−.63	Leg Lift	−.45
Trunk Extension	−.62	Right Grip	−.43

This factor was called maturity lag, since the lack of strength reflected by this factor was not related to a dimensional factor in the factor analysis; it seemed reasonable to assume, therefore, that what was being measured by the second rotated factor was not really a lack of strength but rather a lag in strength. Other studies have substantiated this view. For example, after reviewing the evidence on this subject, Tanner (84) stated: "But there is, it would seem, a period of about a year when a boy, having completed his physical growth, does not have the strength of a young adult of the same body size and shape."

Skeletal Age Relationships

Harrison (56), also reported by Clarke and Harrison (33), examined the relationship between selected physical and motor factors and the skeletal maturity of 9-, 12-, and 15-year-old boys. Each boy was tested within two months of his birthday to provide reasonable homogeneity as far as his chronological age was concerned. The maturity criterion was skeletal age, as determined from X rays of the wrist and hand assessed against the Greulich-Pyle atlas (54). Among the experimental variables were three cable-tension strength tests (elbow flexion, shoulder flexion, and shoulder inward rotation) and the average of 12 cable-tension tests.

Three maturity groups, retarded, normal, and advanced, were established at each of the three ages, based on their skeletal ages. Adjacent groups at each age were separated by one-half to three-quarters of a skeletal-age year. The number of subjects in each group varied from 14 to 19. The differences between the means of the three maturity groups for each of the experimental variables at each age were tested for significance by application of the *t* ratio. The *t* ratios necessary for significance were between 2.03 and 2.05 at the .05 level, since the degrees of freedom for the various comparisons ranged from 28 to 35.

The differences between the means of the cable-tension strength test averages of the boys in the three maturity groups at each of the

Table 6.6

CABLE-TENSION STRENGTH TEST AVERAGES DIFFERENCES
BETWEEN MEANS OF SKELETAL AGE GROUPS

	Means (Pounds)				Mean	S. E.	t
Age	Advanced	Normal	Retarded	df	Diff.	Diff.	Ratio
9	44.31	44.41		34	−.10	1.98	−.05
12	71.12	65.75		30	5.37	4.26	1.26
15	118.59	109.87		28	8.72	6.84	1.27
9	44.31		38.18	30	6.13	2.14	2.86
12	71.12		58.40	28	12.72	3.98	3.20
15	118.59		86.44	30	32.15	6.64	4.84
9		44.41	38.18	32	6.23	1.98	3.15
12		65.75	58.40	28	7.35	2.87	2.56
15		109.87	86.44	30	23.43	6.32	3.71

ages appear in Table 6.6. With the exception of the differences between the means of the advanced and normal maturity groups at nine years of age, the strength means increased with advanced chronological age and maturity. With the exception of the advanced and normal groups, all differences between the strength test means were significant beyond the .05 level; the higher mean was achieved by the more advanced maturity group in each comparison.

The largest and most significant differences in the cable-tension strength means were found between the advanced and retarded maturity groups. For example, at 15 years of age, the means were 118.59 pounds for the advanced group and 86.44 pounds for the retarded group; the difference was 32.15 pounds and the *t* ratio was 4.84. At the ages of 9 and 12 years, the *t* ratios for the differences between these maturity groups were 2.86 and 3.20 respectively.

Comparatively large differences were also found between the mean cable-tension strength test averages for the normal and retarded maturity groups. The *t* ratios for the differences between these means were 3.15, 2.56, and 3.71 for boys at 9, 12, and 15 years respectively.

For the individual muscle groups, although there were several variations, results similar to those found for the cable-tension strength test average were obtained. For elbow flexion strength, the differences between the means of the advanced and normal maturity groups were not significant; the differences between the means of the other comparisons were significant, excepting the means of the normal and retarded groups at 12 years of age. For shoulder flexion strength, the significant differences between means were for the normal and retarded groups at all ages and for all comparisons at 15 years of age. For shoulder inward rotation strength, significant differences between means were found for the advanced and retarded groups at 12 and 15 years of age and the normal and retarded groups at age 15 years.

Pubescent Development Relationships

In another Medford study, Degutis (45), also reported by Clarke and Degutis (29), investigated the relationships between selected physical and motor factors and the pubescent development of 10-, 13-, and 16-year-old boys. Pubescent development was assessed against the criteria proposed by Greulich and associates (53). In this method, the pubescent status of any subject is described in terms of five categories which represent a series of successive stages in the development of the penis, testes, scrotum, and pubic hair. Group 1 resembles the sexual development of a prepubescent boy; Group 5 has reached the external sexual characteristics of an adult. Among the experimental variables were the same cable-tension strength tests included in the skeletal age relationship study above (elbow flexion, shoulder flexion, shoulder inward rotation, and the average of 12 such tests).

The distributions of subjects by pubescent categories for the three ages were as follows:

Pubescent Categories

Age	Group 1	Group 2	Group 3	Group 4	Group 5	Total
10	72	14				86
13	2	25	26	8	4	65
16				12	74	86
						237

Table 6.7

CABLE-TENSION STRENGTH TEST AVERAGES DIFFERENCES BETWEEN
MEANS OF PUBESCENT DEVELOPMENT GROUPS

Age	Means (Pounds)						df	Mean Diff.	S. E. Diff.	t Ratio
	1	2	3	4	4 + 5	5				
10	54.25	58.89					84	4.64	1.49	3.11
13		75.34	81.40				49	6.06	2.46	2.46
		75.34			94.50		35	19.16	5.73	3.35
			81.40		94.50		36	13.10	5.73	2.29
16				112.42		128.01	84	15.59	4.69	3.32

For purposes of this study, the following pubescent groups were formed: age 10 years, groups 1 and 2; age 13 years, groups 2, 3, and 4 + 5; age 16 years, groups 4 and 5. The differences between the means of the pubescent groups for each of the experimental variables at each age were tested for significance by application of the *t* ratio. The *t* ratios necessary for significance at the .05 level were between 1.99 and 2.03, since the degrees of freedom for the various comparisons ranged from 35 to 84.

The differences between the means of the cable-tension strength test averages appear in Table 6.7. At all three ages, the strength means increased with pubescent development. Further, all differences between the means were significant at and beyond the .05 level; the *t* ratios for these differences ranged from 2.29 to 3.35.

The individual cable-tension strength tests did not differentiate between pubescent groups as well as did the average of the 12 strength tests. None of the differences between means was significant at 10 and 16 years of age. For elbow flexion strength at age 13 years, groups 3 and 4 + 5 had means significantly higher than the mean of group 2; the *t* ratios were 3.54 and 3.94, respectively. Further, the mean of group 4 + 5 was nearly significantly higher than the mean of group 3, since the *t* ratio was 1.92. Also, at age 13 years, both the shoulder flexion and shoulder inward rotation means of groups 4 + 5 were significantly higher than the means of group 2; the respective *t* ratios were 2.03 and 2.57.

Cable-Tension Strength Related to Athletic Ability

The relationship between various measures of maturation, physique type, body size, strength, and motor ability and the athletic ability of upper elementary school and junior high school boys has been the subject of three investigations with Medford data. In all instances, levels of athletic ability were differentiated according to success as participants on interschool competitive teams. These differentiations were made by the coaches of the teams at the close of the various sports' seasons. The following rating system was used:

3 Exceptional athletic ability; outstanding performer.
2 Good average player; made first team; played regularly.
1 Out for sport, but did not make first team; a substitute.
NP Nonparticipant.

Elementary and Junior High School Athletes

Petersen (78), also reported by Clarke and Petersen (35), contrasted the maturational, physique, structural, strength, and motor ability characteristics of boys participating on upper elementary school athletic teams (grades five and six) and of boys participating on junior high school athletic teams (grades seven, eight, and nine). The interschool sports were as follows: tackle football, basketball, and track and field for both school levels; baseball for elementary school; wrestling for junior high school; and tennis and golf for ninth grade only. Many of the boys participated in more than one sport; consequently, they received more than one athletic rating. When a boy's ratings for different sports were not the same, he was given the highest rating for purposes of this study.

The number of boys in the study and their athletic ratings were as follows:

Age	3 Rating	2 Rating	1 Rating	NP	Total
		Upper Elementary School			
10	2	5	2	9	18
11	3	8	14	15	40
12	9	6	5	10	30
Total	14	19	21	34	88
		Junior High School			
12			1	9	10
13		10	6	21	37
14	8	8	8	16	40
15	5	7	4	11	27
Total	13	25	19	57	114

Among the test items, the following three cable-tension strength test arrangements were included: cable-tension strength test average (average of 12 tests); upper-body strength (average of elbow flexion, shoulder flexion, and shoulder inward rotation tests); and lower-body strength (average of trunk flexion, trunk extension, and ankle dorsi flexion tests). The differences between the means of the various athletic groups and nonparticipants (NP) at the upper elementary school level and at the junior high school level were tested for significance by application of the t ratio. The t ratios necessary for significance at the .05 level were between 1.99 and 2.04, since the degrees of freedom for the various comparisons ranged from 19 to 62.

The differences between the means of the cable-tension strength test averages of the upper elementary and junior high school athletes and nonparticipants appear in Table 6.8. At both school levels, the outstanding athletes (3) and regular players (2) had significantly

Table 6.8

DIFFERENCES BETWEEN MEAN CABLE-TENSION STRENGTH TEST
AVERAGES FOR ATHLETES AND NONPARTICIPANTS
(in pounds)

| | Athletic Ratings | | | | Mean | S. E. | t |
NP	1	2	3	df	Diff.	Diff.	Ratio
			Upper Elementary School				
52.54	56.36			53	3.82	2.16	1.77
52.54		61.40		51	8.86	3.01	2.94*
52.54			67.34	46	14.80	4.27	3.47*
	56.36	61.40		38	5.04	2.97	1.70
	56.36		67.34	33	10.98	4.24	2.59*
		61.40	67.34	31	5.94	4.73	1.26
			Junior High School				
79.98	88.20			74	8.22	4.64	1.77
79.98		91.90		80	11.92	4.61	2.59*
79.98			110.60	68	30.62	5.73	5.34*
	88.20	91.90		42	3.70	5.80	0.64
	88.20		110.60	30	22.40	6.72	3.33*
		91.90	110.60	36	18.70	6.70	2.79*

* Significant at or above .05 level.

higher means than did the nonparticipants (NP); the respective *t* ratios were 3.47 and 2.94 for the elementary school boys and 5.34 and 2.59 for the junior high school boys. Further, at both levels, the outstanding athletes were significantly superior to the substitutes (1).

For upper-body strength at the elementary school level, all three athletic groups had means significantly higher than the mean of the nonparticipants; the *t* ratios ranged from 2.56 to 3.26. The differences between the means of the athletic groups themselves were not significant, since the highest *t* ratio was .49. At the junior high school level, the means of the outstanding athletes and regular players were significantly higher than the mean of the nonparticipants; the respective *t* ratios were 4.09 and 3.15. In addition, the mean of the outstanding players exceeded the mean of the substitutes; the *t* ratio was 2.01, just significant at the .05 level.

For lower-body strength, the outstanding athletes and regular players had significantly higher means than the nonparticipants at both school levels; the respective *t* ratios were 2.40 and 2.83 for the elementary school boys and 4.66 and 3.84 for the junior high school boys. At the elementary school level, the same athletic groups, also, had significantly higher means than the nonparticipants; the *t* ratios were 1.99 and 2.19 respectively. At the junior high school level, the 3-rated athletes had a significantly higher mean than the 1-rated participants; the *t* ratio for the difference between these means was 2.89. The mean of the 2-rated athletes was higher than the mean of the 1-rated participants, but the difference between means was not significant at the .05 level, since the *t* ratio was 1.86.

In a second Medford study related to athletes, Shelley (83), also reported by Clarke and Shelley (42), concentrated on developing descriptive test profiles of outstanding upper elementary school and junior high school athletes. Inasmuch as the same subjects and the same cable-tension strength tests were included as in the Clarke and Petersen report given above, details of this analysis will not be presented here. The main contributions of this study are to show the test patterns presented by successful individual athletes and to demonstrate ways by which a weakness in one trait found in an athlete are usually compensated for by strength in another.

Upper Elementary School Athletes

With Medford data, Wiley (90) studied 12-year-old elementary school athletes, some of whom had also been subjects of a longitudinal study from the age of nine years. The age of 12 years was chosen because it is generally the oldest elementary school age; thus, logically, this age is also the most favorable one for successful athletic performances at this school level. The cable-tension tests used in this study were for lower-body and upper-body strengths; the test items included were trunk flexion, trunk extension, and ankle dorsi flexion for lower-body strength and elbow flexion, shoulder flexion, and shoulder inward rotation for upper-body strength.

The athletic ratings and classifications were the same as described by Clarke and Petersen above, except that an additional classification was added. When comparing athletic participants in various single sports, a nonparticipant athlete (NPA) classification was included; these boys were nonparticipants in the given sport who participated in one or more other sports.

In analysis of the data, the differences between the means were tested for significance by application of the *t* ratio. The *t* ratios necessary for significance at the .05 level were between 1.97 and 2.09, since the degrees of freedom for the various comparisons ranged from 20 to 200.

SINGLE-AGE ANALYSES. Single-age analyses in Wiley's study were made for the highest athletic rating obtained in all sports, for the athletic ratings awarded in the single sports of football, basketball, baseball, and track and field, and for the athletic ratings given in multiple sports participation.

Football will serve to illustrate the significance of lower-body and upper-body cable-tension strengths of athletes participating in a single sport; the results appear in Table 6.9. For lower-body strength, the outstanding athletes (3) and regular players (2) had significantly higher means than the nonparticipants (NP), nonparticipant athletes (NPA), and substitutes (1); the *t* ratios ranged from 2.22 to 3.02. For upper-arm strength, significant differences between the means favored the outstanding athletes over the nonparticipants, substitutes, and regular players; the *t* ratios ranged from 2.29 to 3.47.

Table 6.9

**DIFFERENCES BETWEEN MEANS OF 12-YEAR-OLD
NONPARTICIPANTS AND FOOTBALL ATHLETES
ON CABLE-TENSION STRENGTH TESTS**
(in pounds)

NP	NPA	*Athletic Ratings* 1	2	3	df	*Mean Diff.*	*S. E. Diff.*	*t Ratio*
		Lower-body Strength						
68.65	62.62				135	6.03	3.71	1.62
68.65		66.65			156	1.98	3.28	.62
68.65			76.18	78.41	166	7.53	3.38	2.22*
68.65					138	9.76	4.25	2.29*
	62.62	66.65			41	4.03	4.41	.91
	62.62		76.18		51	13.56	4.54	2.98*
	62.62			78.41	23	15.79	5.22	3.02*
		66.65	76.18		72	9.52	4.14	2.29*
		66.65		78.41	44	11.76	4.87	2.41*
			76.18	78.41	54	2.23	4.99	.44
		Upper-body Strength						
48.53	53.71				135	5.17	3.06	1.68
48.53		49.01			156	.47	1.99	.23
48.53			51.54		166	3.00	2.08	1.44
48.53				59.68	138	11.14	3.20	3.47*
	53.71	49.01			41	4.69	3.37	1.39
	53.71		51.54		51	2.16	3.42	.63
	53.71			59.68	23	5.97	4.20	1.42
		49.01	51.54		72	2.53	2.51	1.00
		49.01		59.68	44	10.67	3.49	3.04*
			51.54	59.68	54	8.14	3.55	2.29*

* Significant at or above .05 level.

For the other single sports, the significant differences between means are tabulated, as follows:

Basketball

Lower-body strength: 1's over NP's and 2's; t ratios of 2.33 and 2.25.

Upper-body strength: None.

Baseball

Lower-body strength: None.

Upper-body strength: 2's over NP and 3's, NPA's over NP's; t ratios from 1.99 to 2.79.

Track and Field

Lower-body strength: None.

Upper-body strength: 3's over all others; t ratios between 2.11 and 3.96.

When multiple sports participations were considered, the boys rated outstanding in four sports and the boys rated as outstanding or regular players in three sports had significantly higher upper-body strength means than the mean of the nonparticipants; the t ratios were 2.27 and 2.09 respectively. For the lower-body cable-tension average, the 1-rated boys in one sport had a significantly lower mean than the nonparticipants and all other athletic classifications.

LONGITUDINAL ANALYSES. Of the 220 elementary school boys 12 years of age in Wiley's study, only 92 had been tested annually from and including age nine years. As a consequence of this smaller number, the following athletic classifications, only, were justifiable for the longitudinal analyses: NP, or nonparticipants; NPA-1, or nonparticipant athletes and substitutes; and 2-3, or regular players and outstanding athletes. All athletic ratings were made by the coaches when the boys were 12 years old.

Football is again chosen to show the significance of lower-body and upper-body cable-tension strengths in athletic participation in a single sport over a period of four years; the results appear in Table 6.10. For lower-body strength, the outstanding-regular football players had significantly higher means than the NPA-1, not only at 12 years of age but when they were 9 and 10 years old as well; the t ratio was 2.47 at each age. For upper-arm strength, the means

Table 6.10

DIFFERENCES BETWEEN CABLE-TENSION STRENGTH MEANS OF FOOTBALL PLAYERS LONGITUDINAL ANALYSES, AGED TWELVE BACK TO NINE YEARS
(in pounds)

Age	Athletic Ratings			df	Mean Diff.	S. E. Diff.	t Ratio
	NP	NPA-1	2-3				
Lower-body Strength							
12	73.89	71.95		73	1.93	4.00	.47
	73.89		88.65	76	14.76	4.80	3.07*
		71.95	88.65	35	16.69	5.50	3.03*
11	64.03	65.79		71	1.75	3.71	.47
	64.03		68.91	74	4.87	2.74	1.77
		65.79	68.91	35	3.11	4.06	.76
10	56.88	52.81		73	4.07	2.78	1.46
	56.88		62.21	76	5.32	3.45	1.54
		52.81	62.21	35	9.40	3.80	2.47*
9	47.04	43.86		72	3.18	3.00	1.06
	47.04		54.70	76	7.65	4.01	1.90
		43.86	54.70	34	10.84	4.38	2.47*
Upper-body Strength							
12	49.55	46.98		73	2.57	3.11	.82
	49.55		53.46	76	3.90	2.32	1.68
		46.98	53.46	35	6.47	3.31	1.95
11	42.32	40.69		71	1.62	2.30	.70
	42.32		46.05	74	3.73	2.31	1.61
		40.69	46.05	35	5.36	2.62	2.04*
10	38.52	38.60		73	.08	2.05	.03
	38.52		47.55	76	9.03	2.50	3.61*
		38.60	47.55	35	8.95	2.82	3.16*
9	35.23	35.91		72	.68	2.17	.31
	35.23		40.31	76	5.07	2.14	2.36*
		35.91	40.31	34	4.39	2.55	1.71

* Significant at or above the .05 level.

of the 2-3 group were significantly higher than the means of the NPA-1 group at ages 10 and 11 years. This group also had significantly higher means than the NP's when they were 9 and 10 years of age; the *t* ratios were 2.36 and 3.61, respectively.

For the other single sports, none of the lower-body strength means was significant when the subjects were at any age. The upper-body strength means of the 2-3 group were significantly higher than other means as follows:

Basketball: NP group at ages 9 and 10 years; *t* ratios of 2.19 and 2.56.

Baseball: NP group at ages 9 and 10 years; *t* ratios of 2.61 and 3.55.
NPA-1 group at age 10 years; *t* ratio of 2.00.

Track and field: NP group at age 10 years; *t* ratio of 3.66. (Nearly significant at age 9 years; *t* ratio of 1.95.)

Muscular Fatigue Relationships

In the pack-carrying study described in Chapter 5, certain motor-physical fitness tests were given to the college men serving as subjects before the first and after the seventh march of 7.5 miles. For these marches, as well as the others, the fatigue of muscles under stress was measured by use of the Strength Decrement Index (SDI). As a consequence of these evaluations, various muscular fatigue relationships were explored (73).

In addition to providing insight into the nature and magnitude of these relationships, some evidence of the validity of physical-motor fitness tests utilized by the Armed Forces, where pack-carrying is a function of personnel, is presented. In constructing such tests during World War II, validity was based largely upon hypothetical reasoning rather than upon criteria involving the arduous duties Army, Navy, and Air Force personnel must accomplish in the line of duty. In all instances, the basic procedures in validating these tests were as follows: (1) empirical decision to include such motor and physical aspects of fitness as strength, endurance, speed, agility, muscular explosiveness, and the like; (2) theoretical selection of test items, such as chins, dips, runs, etc., to test the motor fitness aspects listed; and (3) relation of the individual test items, singly and in combination, to a composite of the larger number of test items. Thus, for example, with the Army "Physical Efficiency Test," 23 test items were included in the initial experimentation; the final test battery was composed of five of these items. Evidence as to whether these test batteries measure the type of physical condition required of the rifleman (infantry soldier) is inconclusive.

The purpose of this phase of the study was to determine whether the armed services motor fitness tests are correlated to one realistic military requirement, the soldier's endurance in carrying military packs. In addition, certain other motor-physical fitness tests in use in civilian physical education programs were included to determine their value for use in this military situation. These relationships were studied when the subjects were not trained for long marches; and again following a series of seven marches, one week apart, the subjects thus being conditioned somewhat for marching.

Research Procedures

MOTOR-PHYSICAL FITNESS TESTS (14). The motor physical fitness tests included in this study were as follows:

1. Army Physical Efficiency Test. This test was designed to measure the principal factors in general motor fitness designated as strength, endurance, agility, and coordination. The test items were: pull-ups, squat-jumps, push-ups, unlimited sit-ups, and a 300-yard shuttle run.

2. Navy Standard Physical Fitness Test. The Navy test consisted of the following five items: squat thrusts, sit-ups, push-ups, squat jumps, and pull-ups.

3. Air Forces Physical Fitness Test. Three test items composed the AAF motor fitness battery: sit-ups, pull-ups, and 300-yard shuttle run.

4. Strength Index. The Strength Index (SI) is the gross score obtained from lung capacity and the following six strength tests: right grip, left grip, back lift, leg lift, pull-ups, and push-ups (the latter two tests combined in a formula provide an arm strength score).

5. Physical Fitness Index. The Physical Fitness Index (PFI) is a score derived from comparing an achieved Strength Index with a norm based upon the individual's sex, weight, and age.

6. *McCloy Arm Strength Score.* The formula for the McCloy Arm Strength Score is as follows:

Chinning or Dipping Strength =

1.77 (Weight) + 3.42 (No. of Chins or Dips) −.46. In this study, push-ups and pull-ups were combined in the formula.

7. *Over-All Strength Loss.* This measure was obtained by adding the strength losses of all muscle groups for a given march. Thus, this score represents the over-all fatigue effect on muscular strength from the pack-carrying marches.

THE MARCHES. The marching conditions for this study were the same as for the marches described in Chapter 5. Thus, the marching distance was 7.5 miles; the rate of march was 2.5 miles in 50 minutes, followed each time by 10 minutes of rest; testing for Strength Decrement Indices was done during each rest period and at the end of the march; military clothing was worn and military equipment was carried in accordance with Army regulations. Eight muscle groups were tested for strength loss, as follows: shoulder elevators, trunk flexors, trunk extensors, hip flexors, hip extensors, knee flexors, knee extensors, and ankle plantar flexors. The strengths of these muscles were tested with a tensiometer. The SDI's utilized in this study were those obtained at the end of the 7.5-mile marches.

In the original pack-carrying study, the subjects participated in a total of seven marches. For purposes of this study, however, two marches were selected: the third march (the first when the subjects carried complete combat packs), when the subjects were relatively unconditioned for marching; and the seventh march, when the subjects were in their best marching condition, as shown in Chapter 5. The specifications for the two marches were as follows:

> *Third March:* Combat pack, weight, 41 lbs.; pack carried high on back; winter clothing.
> *Seventh March:* Rucksack; weight, 61 lbs.; summer fatigues.

SUBJECTS. The subjects were 32 male students at Springfield College, chosen from the student population. Inasmuch as the sample was composed predominately of physical education majors, it was felt that their performance in the study would be superior where sustained physical effort was required. The following median scores further describe this group: height, 70 in.; weight, 168 lbs.; Physical Fitness Index, 104; and Strength Index, 3013. The age range was from 18.5 to 26.5 years; the median age was 22.2.

STATISTICAL APPLICATIONS. For each march, the Strength Decrement Index for those strength tests showing a significant loss from pack carrying was computed for the subjects. These SDI's were then correlated with each other and with each of the motor fitness tests by means of the Pearson product-moment method. In interpreting these correlations, r's of .35 and .45 are significant at the .05 and .01 levels respectively. The correlations of the strength losses with the test batteries are largely negative, as would be expected from this situation. In explanation, the SDI is reported as a positive figure, but actually indicates the proportionate amount of strength loss; thus, a positive connotation would be a low SDI related to a high test score.

Multiple correlations were computed by the Wherry-Doolittle method (51) with each of the motor-physical fitness tests serving as criterion in turn. Inasmuch as significance for multiple correlations is dependent in part upon the number of variables involved, the following listings are presented for purposes of interpretation.

Predictive indices were utilized to indicate the percentage better than chance relationships for the various correlations obtained.* This statistic is a convenient means of roughly comparing the predictive

Number of Variables	Degrees of Freedom	Coefficient of Multiple Correlation .01 Level	.05 Level
3	29	.43	.51
4	28	.48	.56
5	27	.51	.59
6	26	.55	.62

* The predictive index (also known as the index of forecasting efficiency) is the reverse of Truman Kelly's coefficient of alienation. The fomula: $1 - \sqrt{1 - r^2}$

significance of different coefficients of correlation, especially when N is constant, as in this study.

In order to better understand the various motor-physical fitness tests, the interrelationships of the motor-physical fitness test batteries and items were determined for the last march, when the subjects were in their best condition.

Strength Decrement Relationships

NONCONDITIONED SUBJECTS. The intercorrelations of the SDI's for the third march, when the subjects were relatively unconditioned, were low. The highest such correlation was $-.40$ between trunk flexion and hip extension SDI's; the only other correlation significant at the .05 level was $-.34$ between hip flexion and knee extension SDI's.

Four of the correlations with motor-physical fitness criteria were significant at and beyond the .01 level. Two of these correlations were with knee flexor SDI: $-.59$ with the Army test, and $-.47$ with the AAF test. The other two correlations were obtained with composite SDI: .60 with hip extension SDI, and .53 with knee extension SDI. Also, knee flexion SDI was significantly correlated with the composite SDI at the .05 level (.35).

With the exception of the composite SDI criterion, none of the multiple correlations obtained for this march exceeded the highest product-moment correlations for the various motor-physical fitness batteries. A multiple correlation of .95 resulted from the SDI's for the muscle groups and the composite SDI. This multiple is spuriously high, since the SDI elements were involved in both factors correlated, but it does indicate the most important SDI's in this situation, which were for the following muscle groups: hip extensors, ankle plantar flexors, trunk flexors, and knee extensors.

CONDITIONED SUBJECTS. For the conditioned subjects participating in the final march of the study, the intercorrelations between the SDI's for the various muscle groups and the correlations of these variables with the motor-physical fitness criteria appear in Table 6.11.

Table 6.11

INTERCORRELATIONS OF STRENGTH DECREMENT INDICES AND THEIR CORRELATIONS WITH THE VARIOUS MOTOR-PHYSICAL FITNESS CRITERIA: CONDITIONED SUBJECTS

Item	1 Shldr. Elev.	2 Trunk Flex.	3 Trunk Ext.	4 Hip Flex.	5 Hip Ext.	6 Knee Flex.	7 Ankle Plantar Flex.
Experimental Variables							
1 Shldr. Elev.		.12	.09	.00	−.20	.18	.23
2 Trunk Flex.			.09	.10	.18	−.18	.03
3 Trunk Ext.				−.07	.10	.42	.09
4 Hip Flex.					−.11	.10	.28
5 Hip Ext.						−.09	.09
6 Knee Flex.							.16
Motor-Physical Fitness Criteria							
Army Test	.03	.25	−.03	−.20	.31	−.43	.17
Navy Test	.14	.23	−.16	−.12	.33	−.45	.12
Air Force Test	−.04	.17	−.09	−.19	.24	−.49	.07
Strength Index	−.06	.01	.03	−.20	−.59	−.53	−.16
Physical Fitness Index	.12	.12	.02	−.24	−.03	−.40	−.03
McCloy Arm Strength	−.39	−.15	.00	−.10	−.24	.20	−.14
Composite SDI	.40	.44	.36	.44	.24	.47	.50

For the conditioned subjects, only one of the intercorrelations between the SDI's was significant, the .42 for trunk extension and knee flexion, which nearly reached significance at the .01 level.

Nine of the correlations between SDI's and motor-physical fitness criteria were significant near the .01 level and beyond. Five correlations were significant, or nearly so, at the .05 level. The highest correlation was −.59 between hip extension SDI and the Strength Index.

The most significant feature of this correlational matrix is the prominence of knee flexion SDI. For all but one criterion, the McCloy Arm Strength Score, the correlations with this variable were significant beyond the .05 level (ranging from −.40 to −.53). There is a definite pattern indicating less strength loss of the knee flexor muscles from pack carrying when the subjects have been conditioned for marching with packs.

Five other significant correlations were obtained with composite SDI, as follows: .50 with ankle plantar flexion SDI; .44 with both trunk flexion and hip flexion SDI's; .40 with shoulder elevation SDI; and .36 with trunk extension SDI. A correlation of −.39 was also obtained between the McCloy Arm Strength Score and shoulder elevation SDI.

The distribution of experimental variables (SDI's) as they appeared in the various multiple correlations with motor-physical fitness criteria for the final march is consolidated in Table 6.12.

Conclusions which may be drawn from this table are as follows:

1. The highest multiple correlation was −.92 with the Strength Index as the criterion. This very high inverse relationship indicates definitely that the more gross strength an individual possesses the less proportionate strength loss he will experience from pack-carrying marches up to 7.5 miles.

2. The multiple correlation with Physical Fitness Index is much lower (−.42); the predictive value for SI is six times as great as for PFI. Thus, the relationship between proportionate body strength (for age and weight) and strength loss is low, being statistically significant at the .05 level.

Table 6.12

CONSOLIDATION OF MULTIPLE CORRELATIONS WITH
MOTOR-PHYSICAL FITNESS TESTS FOR THE
FINAL MARCH: CONDITIONED SUBJECTS*

SDI's	SI	PFI	Army Test	Navy Test	AAF Test	McCloy Arm Strength	Composite SDI's
Shoulder Elevation				3		1	6
Trunk Flexion							2
Trunk Extension	3						4
Hip Flexion	4	2					4
Hip Extension	1	1	2	2	2	2	5
Knee Flexion	2		1	1	1	3	3
Ankle Plantar Flexion							1
Multiple R	−.92	−.42	−.49	−.57	−.51	−.49	.88
Predictive Index	.61	.10	.13	.19	.14	.13	.53

* Numbers on chart refer to order in which SDI's appear in the multiple correlations.

3. The highest multiple correlation for the Armed Forces test was −.57, when the Navy test was the criterion; the AAF and Army tests were nearly the same (−.51 and −.49 respectively). Contrasting predictive indices, the SI had 3.2 times greater predictive value than did the Navy test, while the Navy test exceeded the PFI by 90 per cent.

4. The multiple correlation utilizing the McCloy Arm Strength Score as criterion was −.49, the same as for the Army test.

5. The multiple R with composite SDI as the criterion measure was high (.88). This occurrence was expected since the individual SDI's themselves composed the criterion.

6. The following SDI's were of greatest importance in the various multiple batteries:

(a) Knee flexion ranked first in four multiples; second in one; and third in two.

(b) Hip extension appeared second in four multiples; and fifth in one.

(c) Other SDI's ranking first in the multiples were: trunk flexion, for Strength Index; shoulder elevation, for McCloy Arm Strength Score; and ankle plantar flexion, for composite SDI.

Intercorrelations of Motor-Physical Fitness Tests

TEST BATTERIES. The test scores obtained on each of the motor-physical fitness test batteries after the last march, when the subjects were in a conditioned state, were intercorrelated. Table 6.13 contains the results of this analysis.

Relationships among the service tests revealed high intercorrelations of the Army test with the other two: .88 with the Navy test; and .86 with the AAF battery. The correlation between the AAF and the Navy tests, however, was only .48. These tests have common test elements, as follows: pull-ups and sit-ups appear in all three batteries; push-ups and squat jumps, in the Army and Navy tests; 300-yard shuttle run, in the Army and AAF tests; and squat thrusts, in the Navy test only. The Army test has the highest communality with the other two batteries, which may account for its high relationship with each of them. The Army test also correlated .80 with the PFI.

The Strength Index correlated .86 with the Rogers Arm Strength Score; and .83 with the Physical Fitness Index.

The Rogers Arm Strength Score resulted in considerably higher correlations with the various test batteries than did the McCloy Arm Strength Score. The Rogers score correlations with the Navy, Army, and AAF tests were .34, .59, and .69 respectively; while, for the McCloy score, these correlations were .10, −.04, and .14. The correlation between the two arm scores was .46.

Table 6.13

INTERCORRELATION OF MOTOR-PHYSICAL FITNESS TEST: CONDITIONED SUBJECTS

Test	Rogers Arm Str.	SI	PFI	Navy Test	Army Phys. Effic. Test	AAF Test
McCloy Arm Strength	.46	.66	.14	.10	−.04	.14
Rogers Arm Strength		.86	.80	.34	.59	.69
Strength Index			.83	.32	.36	.50
Physical Fitness Index				.49	.80	.63
Navy Fitness					.88	.48
Army Phys. Effic. Test						.86
AAF Test						

TEST ITEMS. Table 6.14 contains the intercorrelations of six of the test items composing the physical-motor fitness tests and the correlations of these items with the various batteries. The spuriousness of certain of these correlations is admitted, when the test item is also a part of a test battery, as in leg lift strength vs. Strength Index and number of situps vs. Army, Navy, or AAF test.

The highest intercorrelations were with leg lift strength: −.57 with time in the 300-yard shuttle run; and .55 with back lift strength. Leg lift strength also correlated high with the following motor-physical fitness criteria: .94 with SI; .82 with PFI; and .66 with Rogers Arm Strength Score.

Table 6.14

INTERCORRELATIONS OF MOTOR-PHYSICAL FITNESS ITEMS AND THEIR CORRELATIONS WITH VARIOUS MOTOR-PHYSICAL FITNESS CRITERIA: CONDITIONED SUBJECTS

Item	Leg Lift	Back Lift	Sit-Ups	300-Yd. Shuttle	Squat Thrusts	Squat Jumps
Experimental Variables						
Leg Lift		.549	-.011	-.570	.029	.072
Back Lift			-.023	-.445	-.109	-.280
Sit-ups				-.261	.482	.483
300-Yd. Run					-.409	-.149
Squat Thrusts						.637
Squat Jumps						
Motor-Physical Fitness Criteria						
AAF Test	.416	.342	.554	-.742	.507	.268
Navy Fitness	.264	.095	.606	-.605	.793	.756
Army Phys. Effic. Test	.342	.129	.632	-.811	.623	.540
Strength Index	.936	.597	.037	-.718	.343	-.093
Physical Fitness Index	.816	.458	-.160	-.658	.437	.074
McCloy Arm Strength	.507	.642	-.149	-.457	-.114	-.202
Rogers Arm Strength	.656	.493	-.046	-.731	.306	.090

Time in the 300-yard shuttle run had significant correlations with all but one of the variables included in Table 6.14. These correlations were −.81 with Army test; −.74 with AAF test; −.73 with Rogers Arm Strength Score; −.72 with SI; −.66 with PFI; −.61 with Navy test; −.57 with leg lift; −.46 with McCloy Arm Strength Score; −.45 with back lift strength; and −.41 with squat thrusts.

The number of squat thrusts performed in one minute was significantly related to the following variables: .79 with Navy test; .64 with squat jumps; .62 with Army test; .51 with AAF test; .48 with unlimited sit-ups; .44 with PFI; and −.41 with 300-yard shuttle run.

For sit-ups, the significant correlations were: .63 with Army test; .61 with Navy test; .55 with AAF test; and .48 with both squat thrusts and squat jumps.

Four correlations were significant for squat jumps: .76 with Navy test; .64 with squat thrusts; .54 with Army test; and .48 with sit-ups.

Multiple correlations were computed utilizing the motor-physical fitness tests as criterion measures and six of the items comprising these test batteries as independent variables. A summary of these correlations appears in Table 6.15.

Table 6.15

CONSOLIDATION OF MULTIPLE CORRELATIONS WITH
MOTOR-PHYSICAL FITNESS TESTS AND ITEMS:
CONDITIONED SUBJECTS

Item	AAF	Navy	Army	SI	PFI
Leg Lift				1	1
Back Lift					
Sit-ups	2		2		3
300-Yd. Run	1	3	1		
Squat Thrusts		1		2	2
Squat Jumps		2	3		
Multiple R	.82	.93	.95	.98	.99

As would be expected, the resultant multiple correlations were very high. The two highest correlations were .99 and .98 for the PFI and SI respectively. In both of these multiples, leg lift strength and squat thrusts were the number 1 and 2 variables; sit-ups was included in the PFI sequence.

For the service tests, the correlations were .95, .93, and .82 for the Army, Navy, and AAF tests in order. The number 1 variable for these multiples was the 300-yard shuttle run for the Army and AAF tests, and squat thrusts for the Navy test; the number 2 variable was sit-ups for the Army and AAF tests, and squat jumps for the Navy test.

Muscular Strength-Endurance Relationships

From the studies pertaining to the development of the cable-tension strengths, to ergographic muscular endurance, and to various other aspects of the subject, muscular strength-endurance relationships were observed (17, 18). These relationships will be stated in this section.

1. *The amount of resistance required to induce muscular exhaustion in a relatively short time varies among individuals, depending on the strength of the muscles primarily involved. The amount of resistance for each subject may be determined as a proportion of that strength.*

In studying methods for single-bout ergographic fatigue testing, reported in Chapter 3, consistent results could be achieved only when ergograph loads were such as to induce exhaustion in a relatively short time, probably in the neighborhood of two minutes. An identical load could not be used for all subjects in such testing if repeatable results were to be obtained. Thus, it became necessary to adapt the amount of the load for each subject. The method found to be effective in determining this amount was to take a proportion of the strength of the muscles to be exercised.

2. *The work output of muscles in exhaustion performances is greater when they are in position to apply greatest tension at the point of greatest stress.*

As shown in Chapters 2 and 3, the strongest position for the application of maximum strength of the elbow flexor muscles is with the forearm midway in the range of motion of the elbow joint. Consequently, in elbow flexion ergography, each movement made in raising the load is initiated from a weak muscular position; and movements are confined to this weak position as exhaustion is approached. For ergographic exercise of these muscles, three-eighths of their strength induces exhaustion in around two minutes. By contrast, greatest strength of the shoulder flexor muscles is achieved with the arm parallel to the body; thus, the joint is in its strongest position at the point of exhaustion in ergographic exercise and each ergographic movement is started from this strong position. For this muscle group, as a consequence, five-eighths proportion of strength is needed to induce exhaustion in the approximately two-minute time.

3. *There appears to be a specific combination (or combinations) of load and speed of movement which produces maximum work output of each muscle group.*

The studies in Chapter 3 pertaining to the conditions of weight loads and cadences for elbow flexion, elbow extension, shoulder flexion, and grip ergography demonstrated that certain combinations of load and speed of movement were superior to others in producing greatest work output for each movement.

4. *Individuals with greatest muscular strength have greatest absolute muscular endurance; however, stronger muscles tend to maintain a smaller proportion of maximum strength in endurance efforts than do weaker muscles.*

Tuttle and associates utilized dynamometers based on the strain-gauge principle for measuring the maximum strength and endurance of the back and leg (87) and grip (88) muscles. Two isometric muscular endurance indices were obtained: an absolute index, as the total area of contractile curve maintained for a specified time; and a relative index, as the average strength maintained for the given time. The correlation between strength and the absolute muscular endurance was .90, and between maximum strength and relative muscular endurance, −.40 and −.48 for back and leg muscles respectively.

Verification of these findings with isotonic exercise is available. A similar negative correlation (−.38 and −.40) between the strength of elbow flexor muscles and their ergographic work output (relative isotonic endurance, inasmuch as loads were adapted to the individual) were obtained by Irish (65) and the writer. Further, the multiple correlation of −.92 between the Strength Index and the SDI's from a pack-carrying march reported earlier in this chapter supports the Tuttle correlation of .90 between strength and absolute muscular endurance. In the pack-carrying study, the same load was carried by all subjects regardless of their strength (thus, absolute muscular endurance was involved); the correlation indicates that the stronger subjects fatigued less.

5. *An immediate effect of fatiguing muscles is to reduce their ability to apply tension. The amount of this decrement is an indicator of the degree of muscle fatigue.*

When the strength-decrement effect on fatigued muscles was studied in Chapter 4, the elbow flexor muscles of the left arm were exercised to exhaustion on the ergograph. The ergographic weight loads were equal to three-eighths proportion of each subject's elbow flexor strength, and cadence was 60, or 30 repetitions per minute. The approximate strength decrements following this exercise for conditioned subjects (college men) were 29 to 33 per cent at 30 seconds, 18 to 20 per cent at 2½ minutes, 8 to 11 per cent at 12½ minutes, and 4 to 5 per cent at 42½ minutes. In the ergographic study by Pastor (77), it is evident that some strength loss occurs very early in fatiguing exercise.

6. *Strength recovery rates following muscular fatigue are improved by muscle condition and by general body movement following exercise.*

In the strength decrement studies reported in Chapter 4, no difference was found between conditioned and unconditioned subjects in the percentage strength loss 30 seconds after exercise. However, the recovery rate was more rapid for the conditioned subjects. Furthermore, for conditioned subjects, the strength recovery at the end of 42½ minutes was greater when the subjects moved about between post-exercise strength tests, thus increasing general body circulation, than when they were supine between these tests—recovery to 4 to 5 per cent below pre-exercise strength means as contrasted with recovery to 10 per cent below.

7. *Muscular fatigue patterns from strenuous total-body activity can be revealed by the strength decrements of individual muscle groups.*

The strength decrements of various muscle groups were utilized to determine muscular fatigue patterns resulting from pack-carrying military marches and from 200-yard time trials in crawl-stroke swimming. In the pack-carrying studies, the strength losses of eleven muscle groups were tested at the end of each 2.5 miles of 7.5-mile marches under field conditions. For each of six marches, such factors as the type of pack, the location of the pack on the body, and the weight of the load carried were varied. A different pattern of muscle groups had strength decrements for the various packs and for changes in the location on the body of the same pack. The degree of fatigue in individual muscle groups was revealed by the amount of this strength loss. Similar results were obtained in determining the fatigue of the muscles of the lower leg and ankle from wearing different military boots and shoes on a standard pack-carrying march, and also when determining the strength decrement of the major muscle groups involved in swimming 200 yards for time.

8. *The strength decrement of involved muscle groups may be used to determine total-body muscular fatigue resulting from strenuous activity, and may serve as a criterion for evaluating the effects of such activity on the body as a whole.*

When the 41-pound combat load of the infantry rifleman was carried on 7.5-mile marches, the total strength decrement of all muscle groups tested was approximately the same whether the pack was carried high or low on the back, although the pattern of affected muscle groups differed. The relationships between the strength losses of muscles from carrying a rucksack with 61-pound load on such a march and various motor-physical fitness tests were determined. The highest multiple correlation obtained was −.92 between strength loss and the Rogers Strength Index. Comparable correlations with the Army, Navy, and Army Air Force motor fitness tests were between −.49 and −.57.

Summary

In this chapter, various muscular strength and muscular fatigue relationships were presented. These studies included: intercorrelations of cable-tension strength tests, with differences attributed to age variations; correlations of strength tests with physical-motor measures, athletic ability, and maturity; muscular fatigue relationships; and muscular strength-endurance relationships.

Chapter **7** / **Discussion**
of Results
and Implications

The purpose of this scientific monograph is to present studies of the volitional muscular strength and muscular endurance of man in which the tensiometer was utilized as the strength testing instrument and an ergograph was used for the measurement of endurance. In this chapter, the results will be discussed and implications from the findings will be drawn.

Application of Strength

Chapter 2 presented an account of the adaptation and utilization of the tensiometer, an instrument originally designed to measure the tension of aircraft controls cables, in the measurement of volitional strength of muscles. In all, 38 strength tests were developed involving finger, wrist, elbow, shoulder, neck, trunk, hip, knee, and ankle joints. For the various joint movements, the strength the muscles can apply with the involved body parts in different positions was tested; also, the strength which muscles can apply throughout the range of motion of activated joints was determined. The tensiometer was demonstrated as a consistent and valid instrument for the testing of muscle strength by cable-tension methods.

These studies of the amount of strength that can be applied by muscles when the body is in different positions and when tested throughout their range of motion provide objective evidence for the following statements: (a) other things being equal, a muscle exerts its greatest strength when it functions at its greatest length; (b) the angle at which the muscle pulls is of importance but usually not of as great importance as its length; (c) the mechanical arrangement of the levers sometimes interferes with the full application of strength, even though the muscles may be at their greatest length; and (d) there probably is an optimum position at which each muscle functions best in the application of strength, and this position may be one in which the tension is optimal (not necessarily maximal) and in which the angle of pull provides for the greatest rotary force.

Stabilizing force, or the force exerted parallel to the long axis of the bone, was not measured in these studies. But in some positions, such as full extension of the knee, this force may be considerable and in addition to the rotary component measured.

Muscular Endurance Manifestations

As a result of their original work in ergography, Helle-brandt and associates (58) concluded that the ergograph may be used to evaluate the initial status of orthopedic patients' disabilities, measure progress under medical treatment, and evaluate the magnitude of residual disability. The ergogram, or kymograph tracing, portrays the subject's performance, so is of primary concern to the therapist. The same may be said for the ergograph exercise of nonhandicapped subjects, when the purpose is not to assess disability but to evaluate the volitional isotonic endurance of particular muscle groups, as shown in Chapter 3.

First of all, the present studies established the fact that loading the ergograph can be accomplished effectively by taking a proportion of the strength of the muscles to be exercised. Thus, the load for isotonic muscular endurance performance was derived from an isometric strength measure. This practice was supported subsequently by others in the objective determination of resistance loads for DeLorme's ten repetitions maximum system of progressive resistance exercise in strength development (47). Clarke (11) and Clarke and Herman (12) found that using a resistance load equal to 50 per cent of knee extension strength was a satisfactory method of determining the amount of weight necessary for ten repetitions maximum in quadriceps muscle development. Clarke and Irving (13) reported that a resistance load of 55 per cent of knee flexion strength was successful in obtaining the desired amount of weight for ten repetitions maximum in exercising the hamstring muscles.

Initially, nonexhaustive ergographic exercise bouts of the elbow flexor muscles were undertaken. With loads that permitted the subjects to continue exercising for two minutes, test-retest correlations between .90 and .95 were obtained. Under these circumstances, kymograph tracings showed complete lifts throughout for light loads and nearly complete lifts throughout for moderate loads. These performances did not indicate when noticeable muscular fatigue took place, so long as complete lifts could be performed. Studies were subsequently conducted of the threshold levels of muscular fatigue from ergographic exercise. Under these conditions, too, no appreciable effects of practice and conditioning upon the results of ergographic testing were observed.

Some difficulty was initially encountered in establishing techniques that would permit adequate testing consistency under conditions of volitional exhaustion performances. Eventually, the test-retest correlations for the various ergographs utilized were established around .85. With exhaustion testing, however, conditioning of the exercising muscles occurred, as revealed by significantly increased strength and endurance means.

Further, it was found that loads for effective ergographic testing required a greater proportion of strength when the exercise movement was initiated from a strong strength position. To illustrate: the strongest point in the elbow flexion movement is midway in the range of motion, not with the elbow straight where the ergographic lift is initiated; for the shoulder flexion movement, the greatest strength is exerted with the arm alongside the body, the position where this ergographic performance starts. With a cadence of 60, or 30 repetitions per minute, three-eighths proportion of strength was satisfactory for elbow flexion ergography, but was totally inadequate for shoulder flexion ergography; for shoulder flexion ergographic testing, a five-eighths proportion was needed. These results prompt another observation relative to the relationship between muscular strength and muscular endurance, as follows: the work output of muscles in exhaustion performances is greater when they are in position to apply greatest tension at the point of greatest stress.

The ergographic conditions of load and cadence for optimum work output were studied for four movements: elbow flexion, shoulder flexion, hand grip, and elbow extension. In general, it was found that the speed of muscular contraction affects muscular endurance performance; there appears to be a specific combination (or combinations) of load and cadence which produces maximum work output of each muscle group. While not always demonstrating significant superiority over other combinations in these studies, each of the following conditions had some advantage: elbow flexion, one-fourth proportion and 76 cadence; shoulder flexion, three-fourths proportion and 84 cadence; grip, one-half proportion and 76 cadence; and elbow extension, one-half proportion and 84 cadence and seven-sixteenths proportion and 52 cadence.

Kymograph tracings effectively portrayed the performances of subjects exercising under various ergographic conditions specified. For example, all tracings for shoulder flexion ergography shown in Figure 3.8 resulted in volitional exhaustion well within the time limit of two minutes imposed. When the strength proportion was three-fourths and the cadence was 84, volitional exhaustion of the subject occurred in 35 seconds; under other conditions, exercising continued for more than twice as long. The point where incomplete lifts occur can readily be seen, as well as the slope of the fatigue gradient. This type of observation may be useful to experimenters desiring to study the effect of varying exercise regimens on muscular strength and endurance development when equivalence in work output and variance in work intensity are needed.

Finally, in Chapter 3, the conditioning effects from ergographic exercise of the elbow flexor muscles were studied. Under the conditions imposed, both muscular strength and muscular endurance improved significantly. No appreciable deconditioning occurred after a four-week lay-off. In a study of the transference of conditioning effects, the mean gain in strength for the nonexercised arm was found to be approximately the same as for the exercised arm; no mean gain in muscular endurance, however, was found for the nonexercised arm.

The conditioning effects of ergographic exercise, as reflected by changes in strength and endurance, should be interpreted only in terms of the experimental conditions imposed. Thus, the ergographic weight loads for the studies reported were equal to three-eighths proportion of the strength of each subject's elbow flexor muscles; the cadence was 60, or 30 repetitions per minute; and exercise continued to volitional exhaustion.

Muscular Fatigue Effects

In Chapter 4, the muscular fatigue effects from volitional exhaustive exercise of the elbow flexor muscles on the Kelso-Hellebrandt ergograph were investigated. The basic hypothesis explored was that an immediate effect of fatiguing muscles is to reduce their contractile power; this hypothesis was fully supported.

Under the conditions imposed (three-eighths strength, 60 cadence, continued to exhaustion), a characteristic mean strength decrement-recovery curve was obtained. The characteristics of this curve are: (a) a pronounced drop in strength (29 to 33 per cent) at 30 seconds after exercise; (b) sharp rise in strength during the next 2½ minutes, continuing at a decelerated rate for an additional 10 minutes, at which time about two-thirds the strength loss had been regained; and (c) a leveling off with continuing slight increase during the next half hour. The correlation between pre-exercise and 30-seconds-after-exercise elbow flexion strength scores was .83. Thus, this relationship indicates considerable consistency in initial strength decrements, although individual differences do exist.

No appreciable difference existed between the percentage decrements of untrained and trained subjects 30 seconds after exercise. However, the trained subjects returned consistently to a higher strength recovery point at the end of 42½ minutes.

The percentage of strength decrements was approximately the same for trained subjects when moving about between strength tests and when moving about and massaging the exercised arm. (It should be observed that the massaging was done by the subject at will and was not a controlled massage situation.) When the subjects were supine between strength tests, however, the mean strength decrement was greater at the end of the post-exercise testing time. Thus, mild general circulation induced from body movement increased the strength recovery rate following exhaustive exercise.

A threshold level of muscular fatigue of the elbow flexor muscles was demonstrated at nine ergographic repetitions when the load was one-fourth strength of the exercising muscles lifted at a cadence of 76, or 38 repetitions, per minute. While the mean strength loss 30 seconds after exercise was significant, the kymograph tracings of the subject portrayed complete lifts during this period.

As a consequence of these ergographic studies, the Strength Decrement Index was proposed as a new measure of muscular fatigue, a useful means of evaluating the effect of local fatigue upon muscle groups (38). Muscle fatigue is accompanied by loss in ability to apply tension; the amount of this loss can be measured, as this amount varies in relation to the degree of fatigue. Consequently, the proportionate strength loss may be utilized as an indicator of the amount of fatigue.

Motivation

Hellebrandt, Skowland, and Kelso (60) have stated that the "dramatic fatigue" from ergographic exercise is predominantly central. They maintain from their extensive experimentation that work falls off not because of diminution in the contractile power of the muscle fibers, but largely by virtue of failure in volitional innervation. Nelson's motivational study described in Chapter 4 supports this conclusion.

The results of Nelson's study demonstrated that applying different motivational situations did affect the performances of college men in stressful physical performance involving exercise to the point of volitional exhaustion on the elbow flexion ergograph. Further, the subjects who exerted more effort in ergographic performances also had greater strength decrements and recovered their strength losses much more slowly.

As shown by measures of variability, considerable variation in ergographic performances was found for the motivational situations. Obviously, then, some subjects were highly motivated and went "all-out," while others made relatively little effort. For example, in the motivational situation using ego-involvement (which also contained a goal), the mean Strength Decrement Index 7½ minutes after exercise was nearly as high as the mean Index 30 seconds after exercise for the three groups composing the low classification. However, for the ego-involvement group, there was a large variation among the 25 subjects in the cumulative distances the ergograph loads were lifted; the standard deviation was 268 cm. and the range was 1126 cm. (between 720 and 1845 cm.).

On the other hand, the ergographic performances of the subjects in the obtainable goal group had very little variation. Most of the subjects reached the goal of 40 repetitions even though the goal was high for the weight load and cadence used.

Strength Decrement Applications

The studies reported in Chapter 5 demonstrated that the Strength Decrement Index could be used effectively to evaluate the muscular fatigue effects resulting from physical activity. The experimental situations involved pack-carrying on military marches, all-out swimming for time, and a submaximal treadmill run. Summaries and conclusions of the results of these studies appear at the ends of the various reports, so will not be given here.

However, the various applications found effective in utilizing the Strength Decrement Index as a measure of muscular fatigue are presented as follows:

1. The degree of muscular fatigue can be measured in relation to the amount of stress imposed. For example, in a given pack-carrying march, strength decrements were greater for some muscles than for others. Also, in swimming 200 yards for time, the shoulder extensor muscles had SDI's of 18 to 22 per cent; these are the muscles that provide arm propulsive force to the swimming stroke.

2. The pattern of muscular fatigue in activities involving total-body performance can be identified. This application was repeatedly demonstrated in the studies reported. For example, in the footgear marching study, significant muscular fatigue of the ankle inverters, everters, and plantar flexors was found when subjects were wearing quarter-cut shoes, but did not occur for the ankle dorsi flexors. The degree of fatigue of each muscle group was also shown.

3. Changes in the degree and pattern of muscular fatigue can be determined when performance conditions are changed. For example, the strength decrement results differed when the men were marching with a combat pack than when marching with a rucksack. For the combat pack, the muscles with greater fatigue were the shoulder elevators and neck extensors; for the rucksack, knee flexion, hip flexion, and trunk flexion muscles showed greater fatigue.

4. The effect of conditioning on the fatigability of muscles can

be determined, provided the stress remains constant. For example, in the first pack-carrying study, marches were performed with the rucksack after considerable conditioning from marching; in the second pack-carrying study, the rucksack was again carried but without the advantage of conditioning. In the first series, the rucksack had a clear advantage when the load was 41 pounds; not until the weight was 61 pounds were strength losses appreciable. On the second series, the 41-pound rucksack march resulted in greater strength decrements; in fact, they were greater than for the combat pack.

Muscular Strength-Endurance Relationships

In Chapter 6, studies of muscular strength-endurance relationships and the relationships of strength to physical-motor fitness, maturity, and athletic ability were presented.

Strength Test Intercorrelations

For upper elementary school boys (and the same was essentially true for junior high school boys), frequently the intercorrelations among strength tests that are antagonists or in the same joint area were among the highest obtained. For example: trunk flexion vs. extension (.809), shoulder extension vs. adduction (.800), hip flexion vs. extension (.753), knee flexion vs. extension (.730). Exceptions were elbow flexion vs. extension (.459) and ankle dorsi flexion vs. plantar flexion (.443). A multiple correlation of .976 was obtained between the average of 18 cable-tension strength tests, as the dependent variable, and shoulder extension, ankle plantar flexion, trunk extension, and knee extension strengths, as the independent variables. Strength test norms based on age and weight were constructed for the composite of these four tests.

The differences between junior high school and upper elementary school boys in the magnitude of the correlations between their cable-tension strength tests varied for some muscle groups. Whenever differences between pairs of intercorrelations for these levels were significant, the junior high school boys had the higher coefficients. Of 12 muscle groups intercorrelated for both school levels, those most frequently involved in the significantly higher correlations of the junior high school boys were elbow flexors, elbow extensors, shoulder flexors, hip flexors, and hip inward rotators.

When intercorrelations for a single age (13 years) were compared with those for the three junior high school ages together, the junior high school boys as a group were found to have significantly higher coefficients in 5 of 66 comparisons. In these instances, either elbow flexion or knee extension strength tests were involved. Thus, with these exceptions, experimentally partialling out the correlational effect of chronological age (by using boys the same age) did not significantly decrease the magnitude of cable-tension strength intercorrelations for junior high school boys as a group.

Physical-Motor Fitness Test Correlations

In several studies, cable-tension strength tests were correlated with various arm strength measures. For junior high school boys, the correlational ranges for McCloy's tests were as follows: Athletic Index, from .73 for shoulder inward rotation to .84 for elbow flexion strength; Push-up Score, from .71 for shoulder flexion to .80 for elbow flexion strength; and Pull-up Score, from .68 for inward rotation to .78 for elbow flexion strength. For the Rogers Arm Strength Score, the range was .57 for shoulder flexion to .75 for shoulder adduction strength. Compared with those of university men, the junior high school correlations were significantly higher for elbow flexion strength with all three McCloy Arm Strength measures; the junior high school correlations were significantly higher also in certain other instances.

For university men, none of the cable-tension strength tests was significantly correlated with distance in the vertical jump, a significant correlation of .30 was obtained between hip extension strength and standing broad jump distance. For junior high school boys, however, the following four correlations with standing broad jump distance were significant: .47 for elbow flexion, .39 for hip extension, .32 for ankle plantar flexion, and .28 for knee extension.

With one exception for university men, correlations were not significant between 16 cable-tension strength tests and the motor fitness items of squat jumps, squat thrusts for one minute and for 12 seconds, and sit-ups for two minutes. For 13-year-old boys, five significant correlations were obtained between cable-tension strength tests and the 60-yard shuttle run; these correlations ranged from −.32 for hip flexion to −.43 for shoulder inward rotation.

Maturity Relationships

In a factor analysis of potential maturity indicators for 13-year-old boys, all 12 cable-tension strength tests included among the experimental variables were significantly correlated with skeletal age. The highest such correlation was .57 for elbow flexion strength. Further, these strength tests had high loadings with a general maturity factor obtained; the loadings ranged from .56 for shoulder inward rotation to .77 for hip inward rotation. Rotated factor II, called maturity lag, had highest loadings with these tests, between .53 and .75.

Three maturity groups, retarded, normal, and advanced, were established at each age, 9, 12 and 15 years, based on their skeletal ages; the differences between the means of the cable-tension strength test average (12 tests) for the maturity groups were determined. These differences were significant between the advanced and retarded and the normal and retarded groups at all ages; for all comparisons, the advanced maturity group had the higher means. Comparable results were obtained when maturity groups were formed on the basis of pubescent development.

Athletic Ability Relationships

Upper elementary and junior high school boys, classified as outstanding athletes, regular players, substitutes, or nonparticipants, were compared on the basis of cable-tension strength tests; the measures were total-body strength (average of 12 tests), lower-body strength (average of three tests), and upper-body strength (average of three tests). At both school levels, the total-body strength means of outstanding athletes and regular players were significantly higher than the means of nonparticipants; with some exceptions, the same was found for lower-body and upper-body strengths.

For upper elementary school 12-year-old boys, the upper-body strength means of outstanding and regular football players were significantly higher than the means of nonparticipants, nonparticipant athletes, and substitutes. For upper-arm strength, significant differences between means favored outstanding athletes over nonparticipants, substitutes, and regular players. Further, for lower-body strength, outstanding and regular football players had significantly higher means than the nonparticipant athletes-substitute group not only at 12 years of age but when they were 9 and 10 years old as well. For lower-body strength, outstanding-regular football players had significantly higher means than the means of nonparticipants when they were 9 and 10 years old and the means of the nonparticipant athlete-substitute group when they were 10 and 11 years of age. Similar comparisons were made for other sports.

Muscular Fatigue Relationships

The relationship between strength decrement from 7.5-mile marches by college men carrying packs, and their scores on various motor-physical fitness tests was studied. While emphasis in this report was placed on the contrast between conditioned and non-conditioned subjects in their pack-carrying effectiveness, two other factors should be kept in mind in comparing the results of the two marches, as follows: (a) the load carried by the conditioned group was 20 pounds heavier than the load carried by the nonconditioned subjects; and (b) rucksacks were carried by the conditioned subjects; the nonconditioned subjects carried regulation combat packs, load in high position. A summary of the results follows:

1. Physical conditioning of the subjects definitely took place during the pack-carrying experiment. Evidences for this conclusion are as follows: (a) the strength of the muscle groups tested increased as the study progressed; (b) the over-all percentage of loss in strength was less, and occurred later, on the final march than on the earlier

march, even though the final march was more strenuous; and (c) significant increases were found in all but one of the motor-physical fitness tests at the termination of the research.

2. The intercorrelations of SDI's for both marches were generally low, none of them quite reaching significance at the .01 level. This result indicates that strength loss in carrying packs on marches with different packs and loads is specific to muscle groups, rather than consistent for all muscle groups primarily involved.

3. For the conditioned subjects on the final march, 14 of the product-moment correlations of SDI's with motor-physical fitness tests were significant. For the nonconditioned subjects on the initial march, five such correlations were significant. Within the limited magnitude of these correlations, these relationships indicate that a high fitness score is accompanied by less strength loss and vice versa.

4. With the exception of the composite SDI, multiple correlations between the SDI's and the different motor-fitness tests were generally very low for the nonconditioned subjects. As a consequence, only meager conclusions are possible in this situation. Two things may account for these results: (a) the load and conditions may not have placed the subjects under sufficient stress for an adequate evaluation of the effects; and (b) the variations in the marching condition of the subjects were such that the effects may have been erratic from subject to subject, thus resulting in lowered correlations.

The final march placed the subjects under greater stress, as they carried 61 pounds, an increase of 50 per cent in weight, but they were definitely improved in physical condition. As a consequence of these considerations, great importance can be placed on the results of the final march in portraying the relationship between strength loss in carrying army packs and the motor-physical fitness tests. Comments below relate to the conditioned subjects only.

5. The Strength Index as criterion produced by far the highest multiple correlation $(-.92)$ obtained for any of the motor-physical fitness tests (excluding composite SDI). Consequently, the Strength Index is definitely superior to the other tests investigated in predicting muscle fatigue, as reflected in strength loss, from carrying military packs under the field conditions of this experiment.

6. Comparing the armed services motor fitness batteries, the Navy test was found superior to both the Army and the AAF tests in evaluating strength loss from pack carrying. However, the multiple correlation obtained for this test was far too low for predictive purposes ($-.57$).

7. The McCloy Arm Strength Score produced a multiple correlation within the same range as the armed services tests. The Physical Fitness Index had a lower multiple correlation than did McCloy's score.

8. The individual SDI's which were most prominent in the multiple correlations were knee flexors and hip extensors. Apparently, therefore, the strength loss of these muscle groups from pack-carrying marches best reveals the general condition of the subjects. However, the muscle groups reflecting over-all strength loss are ankle plantar flexors, trunk flexors, and knee flexors, as these had ranking positions in the multiple correlation with the composite SDI.

9. The Army motor fitness test correlated well with the other two service tests for conditioned subjects, as follows: .88 with the Navy test; and .86 with the AAF battery. The correlation between the Navy and AAF tests, however, was much lower (.48). The Strength Index correlated .86 with the Rogers Arm Strength Score; and .83 with the Physical Fitness Index. The Rogers Arm Strength Score resulted in considerably higher correlations with the various test batteries than did the McCloy Arm Strength Score.

10. The three most significant tests resulting from an intercorrelation of six of the individual tests composing the motor-physical fitness batteries and the correlation of these items with the various batteries were as follows:

(a) Leg lift strength: .94 with Strength Index; .82 with Physical Fitness Index; and .66 with Rogers Arm Strength Score.
(b) Time in the 300-yard run: $-.81$ with Army test; $-.74$ with AAF test; $-.73$ with Rogers Arm Strength Score; $-.72$ with Strength Index; $-.66$ with Physical Fitness Index; and $-.61$ with Navy test.
(c) Number of squat thrusts in one minute: .79 with Navy test; .65 with squat jumps; and .62 with Army test.

11. With subjects conditioned for marching with packs, the following multiple correlations were obtained between each of the motor-physical fitness tests as criterion and six of the items comprising these batteries:

(a) Physical Fitness Index, .99; leg lift, squat thrusts, and sit-ups.
(b) Strength Index, .98: leg lift and squat thrusts.
(c) Army Physical Efficiency Test, .95: 300-yard shuttle run, sit-ups, and squat jumps (.92 without squat jumps).
(d) Navy Standard Physical Fitness Test, .93: squat thrusts, squat jumps, and 300-yard shuttle run (.85 without run).
(e) Army Physical Efficiency Test, .95: 300-yard shuttle run, and sit-ups.

Muscular Strength-Endurance Relationships

Based on studies reported throughout this monograph, the following eight muscular strength-endurance relationships were formulated:

1. The amount of resistance required to induce muscular exhaustion in a relatively short time varies among individuals, depending on the strength of the muscles primarily involved. The amount of resistance for each subject may be determined as a proportion of that strength.

2. The work output of muscles in exhaustion performances is greater when they are in position to apply greatest tension at the point of greatest stress.

3. There appears to be a specific combination (or combinations) of load and speed of movement which produces maximum work output of each muscle group.

4. Individuals with greatest muscular strength have greatest absolute muscular endurance; however, stronger muscles tend to maintain a smaller proportion of maximum strength in endurance efforts than do weaker muscles.

5. An immediate effect of fatiguing muscles is to reduce their ability to apply tension. The amount of this decrement is an indicator of the degree of muscle fatigue.

6. Strength recovery rates following muscular fatigue are improved by muscle condition and by general body movement following exercise.

7. Muscular fatigue patterns from strenuous total-body activity can be revealed by the strength decrements of individual muscle groups.

8. The strength decrement of involved muscle groups may be used to determine total-body muscular fatigue resulting from strenuous activity, and may serve as a criterion of such activity on the body as a whole.

BIBLIOGRAPHY

1. Appleton, Lloyd O., "The Relationship Between Physical Ability and Success at the United States Military Academy," Doctoral Dissertation, New York University, 1949.
2. Bailer, E. M., *Content and Form in Tests of Intelligence*. New York: Teachers College, Columbia University, 1925.
3. Bailey, Theodore L., and William H. McDermott, *Review of Research on Load Carrying*. Tentage and Equipment Series No. 9, Office of the Quartermaster General, Department of the Army, 1952.
4. Beasley, Willis C., "Instrumentation and Equipment for Quantitative Clinical Muscle Testing," *Archives of Physical Medicine and Rehabilitation*, 37, No. 10 (October, 1956), pp. 604–621.
5. Brezina, E., and H. Reichel, "Energy Exchange During Marching: Marching upon a Horizontal Road," *Biochemische Zeitschrift*, 63 (1914), p. 107.
6. Burt, John J., "Factor Analysis of Potential Maturity Indicators of Thirteen-Year-Old Boys," Doctoral Dissertation, University of Oregon, 1962.
7. Carlson, L. D., and A. W. Martin, "A Method of Studying Reflex Activity Under Varying Conditions," *Federation Proceedings*, 7, No. 1 (March, 1948), pp. 18–19.
8. Carve, Lt., *Historical Review of the Load of the Foot Soldier*. Tentage and Equipment Series No. 8, Office of the Quartermaster General, Department of the Army. (Translated by Captain P. L. Miles for publication in the *Infantry Journal*, 1908.)
9. Cathcart, E. P., D. T. Richardson, and W. C. Campbell, "The Maximum Load to Be Carried by a Soldier," *Journal of Royal Army Medical Corps*, 40: 435; 41: 87 (1923).
10. Clarke, David H., "Strength Recovery of the Elbow Flexor Muscles after Ergographic Exhaustive Exercise," Master's Thesis, Springfield College, 1953.
11. ————, "The Application of Measurement to Quadriceps Exercise Prescriptions," *Journal of Association for Physical and Mental Rehabilitation*, 11, No. 2 (March–April, 1957), pp. 48–50.
12. ————, and Edward L. Herman, "Objective Determination of Resistance Load for Ten Repetitions Maximum for Quadriceps Development," *Research Quarterly*, 26, No. 4 (December, 1955), pp. 385–390.

13. ———, and Robert N. Irving, "Objective Determination of Resistance Load for Ten Repetitions Maximum for Knee Flexion Exercise," *Research Quarterly*, 31, No. 2 (May 1960), pp. 131–135.

14. Clarke, H. Harrison, *Application of Measurement to Health and Physical Education*, 3rd ed. Englewood Cliffs, N.J.: Prentice-Hall, Inc., 1959.

15. ———, "Comparison of Instruments for Recording Muscle Strength," *Research Quarterly*, 25, No. 4 (December, 1954), pp. 398–411.

16. ———, "Improvement of Objective Strength Tests of Muscle Groups by Cable-Tension Methods," *Research Quarterly*, 21, No. 4 (December, 1950), pp. 399–419.

17. ———, "Muscular Strength-Endurance Observations from Single-Bout Ergography," *Journal of Association for Physical and Mental Rehabilitation*, 7, No. 1 (January–February, 1953), pp. 8–11.

18. ———, "Muscular Strength-Endurance Relationships," *Archives of Physical Medicine and Rehabilitation*, 38, No. 9 (September, 1957), pp. 584–586.

19. ———, "Objective Strength Tests of Affected Muscle Groups Involved in Orthopedic Disabilities," *Research Quarterly*, 19, No. 2 (May, 1948).

20. ———, "Precision of Elbow Flexion Ergography Under Varying Degrees of Muscular Fatigue," *Archives of Physical Medicine*, 33, No. 5 (May, 1952), pp. 277–288.

21. ———, "Relation of Physical Structure to Motor Performance of Males," *American Academy of Physical Education*, Professional Contributions No. 6 (November, 1958), pp. 63–74.

22. ———, "Relationships of Strength and Anthropometric Measures to Physical Performances Involving the Trunk and Legs," *Research Quarterly*, 28, No. 3 (October, 1957), pp. 223–232.

23. ———, "Relationship of Strength and Anthropometric Measures to Various Arm Strength Criteria," *Research Quarterly*, 25, No. 2 (May, 1954), p. 134–143.

24. ———, "Single-Bout Elbow Flexion and Shoulder Flexion Ergography Under Conditions of Exhaustion Testing," *Archives of Physical Medicine and Rehabilitation*, 34, No. 4 (April, 1953), pp. 240–246.

25. ———, "Strength Decrement of Trunk and Lower Extremities from Sub-Maximal Treadmill Running," *Research Quarterly*, 28, No. 2 (May, 1957), pp. 95–99.

26. ———, and Theodore L. Bailey, "Strength Curves for Fourteen Joint Movements," *Journal of Association for Physical and Mental Rehabilitation*, 4, No. 2 (April–May, 1950), pp. 12–16.

27. ———, Theodore L. Bailey, and Clayton T. Shay, "New Objective Strength Tests of Muscle Groups by Cable-Tension Methods," *Research Quarterly*, 23, No. 2 (May, 1952), pp. 136–148.

28. ———, and David H. Clarke, *Developmental and Adapted Physical Education*. Englewood Cliffs, N.J.: Prentice-Hall, Inc., 1963, pp. 73–78.

29. ———, and Ernest W. Degutis, "Comparison of Skeletal Age and Various Physical and Motor Factors with the Pubescent Development of 10, 13, and 16-Year-Old Boys," *Research Quarterly*, 33, No. 3 (October, 1962), pp. 356–368.

30. ———, Earl C. Elkins, Gordon M. Martin, and Khalil C. Wakim, "Relationship Between Body Position and the Application of Muscle Power to Movements of the Joints," *Archives of Physical Medicine*, 31, No. 2 (February, 1950), pp. 81–89.

31. ———, and Arthur A. Esslinger, "Medford Boys' Growth Study," *Northwest Medicine*, 57, No. 9 (September, 1958), pp. 1197–1198.

32. ———, and Don Glines, "Relationships of Reaction, Movement, and Completion Times to Motor, Strength, Anthropometric, and Maturity Measures of 13-Year-Old Boys," *Research Quarterly*, 33, No. 2 (May, 1962), pp. 194–201.

33. ———, and James C. E. Harrison, "Differences in Physical and Motor Traits Between Boys of Advanced, Normal, and Retarded Maturity," *Research Quarterly*, 33, No. 1 (March, 1962), pp. 13–25.

34. ———, Everett A. Irish, Garland A. Trzynka, and William Popovich, "Conditions for Optimum Work Output in Elbow Flexion, Shoulder Flexion, and Grip Ergography," *Archives of Physical Medicine and Rehabilitation*, 39, No. 8 (August, 1958), pp. 475–481.

35. ———, and Kay H. Petersen, "Contrast of Maturational, Structural, and Strength Characteristics of Athletes and Non-Athletes 10 to 15 Years of Age," *Research Quarterly*, 32, No. 2 (May, 1961), pp. 163–176.

36. ———, and Theodore G. Schopf, "Construction of a Muscular Strength Test for Boys in Grades 4, 5, and 6," *Research Quarterly*, 33, No. 4 (December, 1962), pp. 515–522.

37. ———, Clayton T. Shay, and Donald K. Mathews, "Strength and Endurance (Conditioning) Effects of Exhaustive Exercise of the Elbow Flexor Muscles," *Journal of Association for Physical and Mental Rehabilitation*, 8, No. 6 (November–December, 1954), pp. 184–188.

38. ———, Clayton T. Shay, and Donald K. Mathews, "Strength Decrement Index: A New Test of Muscle Fatigue," *Archives of Physical Medicine and Rehabilitation*, 36, No. 6 (June, 1955), pp. 376–378.

39. ———, Clayton T. Shay, and Donald K. Mathews, "Strength Decrement of Elbow Flexor Muscles Following Exhaustive Exercise," *Archives of Physical Medicine and Rehabilitation*, 35, No. 9 (September, 1954), pp. 560–566.

40. ———, Clayton T. Shay, and Donald K. Mathews, "Strength Decrements from Carrying Various Army Packs on Military Marches," *Research Quarterly*, 26, No. 3 (October, 1955), pp. 253–265.

41. ———, Clayton T. Shay, and Donald K. Mathews, "Strength Decrements from Wearing Various Army Boots and Shoes on Military Marches," *Research Quarterly*, 26, No. 3 (October, 1955), pp. 266–272.

42. ———, and Morgan E. Shelley, "Maturity, Structure, Strength, Motor Ability, and Intelligence Test Profiles of Outstanding Elementary School and Junior High School Athletes," *Physical Educator*, 18, No. 4 (December, 1961), pp. 132–137.

43. Daniels, Lucile, Marian Williams, and Catherine Worthingham, *Muscle Testing*. Philadelphia: W. B. Saunders Co., 1947, pp. 9–13.

44. Davis, Jack F., "Effects of Training and Conditioning for Middle Distance Swimming upon Measures of Cardiovascular Condition, General Physical Fitness, Gross Strength, Motor Fitness, and Strength of Involved Muscles," Doctoral Dissertation, University of Oregon, 1955.

45. Degutis, Ernest W., "Relationships Between Selected Physical and Motor Factors and the Pubescent Development of Ten, Thirteen, and Sixteen Year Old Boys," Doctoral Dissertation, University of Oregon, 1960.

46. ———, "Relationships Between the Standing Broad Jump and Various Maturity, Structural, and Strength Measures of Twelve-Year-Old Boys," Master's Thesis, University of Oregon, 1959.

47. DeLorme, Thomas L., and Arthur L. Watkins, *Progressive Resistance Exercise: Technic and Medical Application*. New York: Appleton-Century-Crofts, Inc., 1951, pp. 23–28.

48. ———, "Restoration of Muscle Power by Heavy-Resistive Exercise," *Journal of Bone and Joint Surgery*, 27, No. 4 (October, 1945), p. 645.

49. Elbel, Edwin R., "A Study in Short Static Strength of Muscles," Master's Thesis, Springfield College, 1928.

50. Franz, Shepherd I., "On the Method of Estimating the Force of Voluntary Muscular Contractions and on Fatigue," *American Journal of Physiology*, 5, No. 7 (October, 1900), p. 348.

51. Garrett, Henry E., *Statistics in Education and Psychology*, 5th ed. New York: David McKay Co., Inc., 1958, p. 426.

52. Glines, Don, "Relationships of Reaction, Movement, and Completion Times to Certain Motor, Strength, Anthropometric, and Maturity Measures," Doctoral Dissertation, University of Oregon, 1960.

53. Greulich, W. W., R. I. Doufman, H. R. Catchpole, C. I. Solomon, and C. S. Culotte, "Somatic and Endocrine Studies of Puberal and Adolescent Boys," *Monograph of the Society For Research in Child Development*, 7 (1942), pp. 1–74.

54. ———, and S. I. Pyle, *Radiographic Atlas of Skeletal Development of the Hand and Wrist*. Stanford, Calif.: Stanford University Press, 1950.

55. Hall, Winfield S., "A New Form of Ergograph," *American Journal of Physiology*, 6, No. 7 (March, 1902), p. xxiii.

56. Harrison, James C. E., "The Relationships Between Selected Physical and Motor Factors and the Skeletal Maturity of Nine, Twelve, and Fifteen-Year-Old Boys," Doctoral Dissertation, University of Oregon, 1959.

57. Hellebrandt, F. A., Sara J. Houtz, and L. E. A. Kelso, "New Devices for Disability Evaluation: 3. The Grip Ergograph," *Archives of Physical Medicine*, 31, No. 4 (April, 1950), pp. 207–212.

58. ———, L. E. A. Kelso, Sara J. Houtz, and R. N. Eubank, "New Devices for Disability Evaluation: 2. The Thumb Ergograph," *Archives of Physical Medicine*, 31, No. 4 (April, 1950), pp. 201–206.

59. ———, and Helen V. Skowland, "The Application of Ergography to Disability Evaluation: I. The Normal Fatigue Curve," *American Journal of Occupational Therapy*, 1, No. 2 (April, 1947), p. 73.

60. ———, Helen V. Skowland, and L. E. A. Kelso, "New Devices for Disability Evaluation: 1. Hand, Wrist, Radioulnar, Elbow and Shoulder Ergographs," *Archives of Physical Medicine*, 29, No. 1 (January, 1948), pp. 21–28.

61. Holmes, Jesse G., "The Capacity of a Human Muscle for Work," *Journal of American Medical Association*, 41, No. 25 (December 19, 1903), p. 1532.

62. Hough, Theodore, "Ergographic Studies in Neuro-Muscular Fatigue," *American Journal of Physiology*, 5, No. 4 (May, 1901), p. 240.

63. Hunsicker, Paul A., "Arm Strength at Selected Degrees of Elbow

Flexion," Air Force Project No. 7214–71727, WADC TR 54–548, Wright-Patterson Air Force Base, 1954.

64. ——, and Richard L. Donnelly, "Instruments to Measure Strength," *Research Quarterly*, 26, No. 4 (December, 1955), pp. 408–420.

65. Irish, Everett A., "Optimum Endurance Measurement of Elbow Flexor Muscles and the Relations of Strength, Anthropometric, and Fatigue Factors to Arm Strength Criteria," Doctoral Dissertation, University of Oregon, 1958.

66. Jones, Harold E., *Motor Performance and Growth*. Berkeley: University of California Press, 1949.

67. Karpovich, Peter V., *Physiology of Muscular Activity*, 5th ed. Philadelphia: W. B. Saunders Co., 1959, p. 235.

68. Kraus, Hans, and Wilhelm Raab, *Hypokinetic Disease*. Springfield, Ill.: Charles C Thomas, Publisher, 1961.

69. Lewis, Thomas, George W. Pickering, and Paul Rothschild, "Observations Upon Muscular Pain in Intermittent Clandication," *Heart*, 15 (July, 1931), p. 359.

70. Lovett, R. W., and E. C. Martin, "Certain Aspects of Infantile Paralysis with a Description of a Method of Muscle Testing," *Journal of American Medical Association*, 66, No. 10 (March 4, 1916), p. 729.

71. Maitz, H. P., and C. P. N. Sinha, "Studies in Muscular Work by the Ergographic Method," *Indian Journal of Psychology*, 1 (1926), pp. 48–52.

72. Marks, Eli S., "Individual Differences in Work Curves," *Archives of Psychology*, 7 (May, 1935), p. 5.

73. Mathews, Donald K., Clayton T. Shay, and H. Harrison Clarke, "Relationship Between Strength Loss in Pack Carrying and Certain Motor-Physical Fitness Criteria," *Research Quarterly*, 26, No. 4 (December, 1955), pp. 426–439.

74. Mosso, A., *Fatigue*, trans. M. and W. B. Drummond. New York: G. P. Putnam's Sons, 1906, p. 84.

75. Nelson, Jack K., "An Analysis of the Effects of Applying Various Motivational Situations to College Men Subjected to a Stressful Physical Performance," Doctoral Dissertation, University of Oregon, August, 1962.

76. Newman, L. B., "A New Device for Measuring Muscle," *Archives of Physical Medicine*, 30, No. 4 (April, 1949), pp. 234–237.

77. Pastor, Paul J., "Threshold Muscular Fatigue Level and Strength Decrement Recovery of Elbow Flexor Muscles Resulting from Various Degrees of Muscular Work," Doctoral Dissertation, University of Oregon, 1958.

78. Petersen, Kay H., "Contrast of Maturity, Structural, and Strength Measures Between Non-Participants and Athletic Groups of Boys Ten to Fifteen Years of Age," Doctoral Dissertation, University of Oregon, 1959.

79. Ralston, H. J., and others, "Mechanics in Human Isolated Voluntary Muscle," *American Journal of Physiology*, 151, No. 2 (December, 1947), pp. 612–620.

80. Reiser, Kenneth W., "Load and Cadence for Optimum Work Output in Single-Bout Elbow Extension Ergography under Conditions of Exhaustion Testing," Master's Thesis, University of Oregon, 1959.

81. Rogers, Frederick Rand, *Physical Capacity Tests in the Administration of Physical Education*. New York: Teachers College, Columbia University, 1926.

82. Schopf, Theodore G., "Construction of a Muscular Strength Test for Boys in Grades Four, Five, and Six," Doctoral Dissertation, University of Oregon, 1961.

83. Shelley, Morgan E., "Maturity, Structure, Strength, Motor Ability, and Intelligence Test Profiles of Outstanding Elementary School and Junior High School Athletes," Master's Thesis, University of Oregon, 1960.

84. Tanner, J. M., *Growth at Adolescence*, 2nd ed. Springfield, Ill.: Charles C Thomas, Publisher, 1962, p. 204.

85. Tin, Co, and others, "The Construction and Use of a Bedside Ergograph," *Annals of Surgery*, 120, No. 1 (July, 1944), p. 123.

86. Tomaras, William A., "The Relationship of Anthropometric and Strength Measures of Junior High School Boys to Various Arm Strength Criteria," Doctoral Dissertation, University of Oregon, 1958.

87. Tuttle, W. W., C. D. Janney, and J. V. Salzano, "Relation of Maximum Back and Leg Strength to Back and Leg Endurance," *Research Quarterly*, 26, No. 1 (March, 1935), pp. 96–106.

88. ———, C. D. Janney, and C. W. Thompson, "Relation of Maximum Grip Strength to Grip Strength Endurance," *Journal of Applied Physiology*, 2, No. 12 (June, 1950), pp. 663–670.

89. Wakim, Khalil G., Jerome W. Gersten, Earl C. Elkins, and Gordon M. Martin, "Objective Recording of Muscle Strength," *Archives of Physical Medicine*, 31, No. 2 (February, 1950), pp. 90–99.

90. Wiley, Roger C., "Single-Year and Longitudinal Comparisons of Maturity, Physique, Structural, Strength, and Motor Characteristics of Twelve-Year-Old Elementary School Athletes and Non-participants," Doctoral Dissertation, University of Oregon, 1963.